EMERGENCY MEDICAL TECHNICIAN–PARAMEDIC
EXAMINATION REVIEW

EMERGENCY MEDICAL TECHNICIAN PARAMEDIC
EXAMINATION REVIEW

---

600 QUESTIONS WITH EXPLANATORY ANSWERS

Charles E. Stewart, MD, FACEP
Director of Research and Education
Regional Medical Director
Spectrum Emergency Care, Inc.
St. Louis, Missouri

Carol P. Stewart, RN
Consultant, Medical Education
  and Editing
Colorado Springs, Colorado

MEDICAL EXAMINATION PUBLISHING COMPANY

Copyright © 1989 by Elsevier Science Publishing Co., Inc.
Medical Examination Publishing Company
A division of Elsevier Science Publishing Co., Inc.
655 Avenue of the Americas, New York, New York 10010

Stewart, Charles E. (Charles Edward), 1947-
    Emergency medical technician-paramedic: examination review: 600 questions with explanatory answers / Charles E. Stewart, Carol Stewart.

    p.   cm.

    Bibliography: p.

    ISBN 0-444-01481-0

    1. Emergency medicine - Examinations, questions, etc. 2. Emergency medical technicians - Examinations, questions, etc. 3. Ambulance service - Examinations, questions, etc. I. Stewart, Carol. II. Title.
(DNLM: 1. Allied Health Personnel - examination questions.
    2. Emergency Medicine - examination questions. WB 18 S849e)

RC86.9.S74   1989

618'.025'076 - dc19

DNLM/DLC

for Library of Congress   89-3123

Current printing (last digit)   CIP
10 9 8 7 6 5 4 3

Printed in the United States of America

Contents

Preface

Emergency Medical Technician – Paramedic Examination Review is designed to help you prepare for course examinations and state licensure examinations for EMT-P certification. It is based in large part on experience in teaching paramedics in several states over 12 years.

The range of subjects in this volume is based on the content outline of the Department of Transportation guidelines for the paramedic course. Advanced Cardiac Life Support (ACLS) questions are based upon the American Heart Association (AHA) 1986 Standards as published in the *Journal of the American Medical Association* and the AHA ACLS textbook.

The questions, organized in broad categories, give a representative sampling of the material covered in course work, and help you define which areas will need additional attention. A large question pool of state and local certifying examinations was examined to ensure that the style, format, and content of the questions are similar and complete. Since the bulk of these examinations are multiple choice, this format comprises the majority of the questions. For your convenience in selective study, the answers, together with commentary and references, follow each section of questions.

Using this book, you may identify areas of strength and weakness in your command of the subjects presented. Specific references to widely used texts allow you to turn to the source for further study. Commentary updates and expands the text where new information has been added. The questions and answers, taken together, emphasize problem solving rather than rote or lore. Retention of factual knowledge is placed in a perspective of hands-on care.

Acknowledgments

Grateful appreciation is made to our two daughters who had to listen to "how does this sound" too many times to be believed. Their patience, cooperation, and enthusiasm for life has been a joy to behold. They added their unique perspective to several answers and commentaries. Our experiences with them prompted many questions found in this text.

A distinctive thank you goes to Kenneth Phillips, PAC, who literally heard and reviewed every word of this text. His comments and reflections about field emergency medicine were invaluable.

Our hat also goes off to the many "unsung" heroes who brought patients in while I was working, and had to listen to a question at 3 AM — just to see how it went. I particularly appreciated the help given by scores of paramedics in Colorado Springs, Denver, Pueblo, North and South Dakota, Wyoming, California, Pennsylvania, West Virginia, Ohio, North Carolina, Maryland, Oregon, and Washington for sending me sample questions, thoughts, and criticism about how it is written versus how it is done in the field. I was especially grateful to Swedish Medical Center in Denver and The Center for Emergency Medicine in Pittsburgh, both of which graciously allowed me to review questions from their paramedic training courses, and to Saint Anthony's Medical Center in Denver, which likewise provided ACLS instructional materials.

Of exceptional help in this was the original guidance of Peter Safar, MD; Don Benson, MD; William Robinson, MD; Mitch Brown; and David Lindell of Pittsburgh, who helped a fledgling medical student to get his training with the paramedics of Freedom House Ambulance Service in the streets of Pittsburgh. Their model lives in each and every paramedic today as the Department of Transportation guidelines. My friends, Ron, the "other" Dr. Stewart, and Paul Paris, MD, honed and sharpened this role model with guidance in clinical writing and research at the Center for Emergency Medicine. The respect and friendship of these folks will not be forgotten.

C.E.S.

1 Anatomy and Physiology

QUESTIONS 1–43: Select the ONE most appropriate answer.

1. What are the three types of muscle?
   A. Voluntary, involuntary, cardiac
   B. Smooth, involuntary, voluntary
   C. Smooth, striated, cardiac
   D. Striated, voluntary, involuntary

2. What label is given to the amount of blood that is ejected during a ventricular contraction?
   A. Stroke volume
   B. Heart rate
   C. Cardiac output
   D. End-diastolic phase
   E. Peripheral resistance

3. The volume of air inhaled during one breath is called the
   A. respiratory rate
   B. minute volume
   C. residual volume
   D. tidal volume
   E. stroke volume

4. What region of the brain is responsible for the automatic responses such as respirations, cardiac function and blood vessel control?
   A. Pituitary
   B. Medulla oblongata
   C. Cerebellum
   D. Cerebrum

5. Cardiac output depends on which of the following:
   1. Resistance to blood flow
   2. Heart rate
   3. Pressure in the system
   4. Stroke volume (the volume of blood the heart pumps out with each beat)
      A. 1,2, and 3
      B. 2,3, and 4
      C. 2 and 4
      D. 4 only
      E. All of the above

6. The sensation of shortness of breath is called
   A. apnea
   B. dyspnea
   C. tachypnea
   D. hyperpnea
   E. bradypnea

7. A profusely perspiring individual is
   A. dyspneic
   B. erythematous
   C. diaphoretic
   D. distended
   E. hyperpenic

8. Osmotic pressure is dependent on
   A. the pumping action of the heart
   B. protein concentration of intravascular fluid
   C. glucose concentration in extracellular space
   D. the action of the sympathetic nervous system
   E. none of the above

9. The movement of particles from an area of greater concentration to that of lesser concentration across a selectively permeable membrane is known as
   A. osmosis
   B. diffusion
   C. hycosamine
   D. homeostasis
   E. hyperhydriosis

10. Diffusion of water from an area of lower concentration to an area of higher concentration is known as
   A. osmosis
   B. diffusion
   C. hycosamine
   D. homeostasis
   E. hyperhydriosis

11. The fluid of the lymphatic system is called
   A. cerebrospinal fluid
   B. Dextran
   C. lymph
   D. plasma
   E. exudate

12. The fluid or liquid portion of the blood is called
   A. Dextran
   B. albumin
   C. cytoplasm
   D. plasma
   E. lymph

13. The heart has four chambers. The two inferior chambers are called
   A. atria
   B. ventricles
   C. auricles
   D. A or C
   E. the conduction pathway of His

14. The adrenal medulla
   A. produces epinephrine
   B. blocks the sympathetic nervous system
   C. is important for the fight-or-flight response
   D. receives stimulus from the pituitary gland
   E. A and C

15. The gland that is primarily responsible for metabolic regulation is the
   A. pituitary gland
   B. parathyroid gland
   C. thyroid gland
   D. adrenal gland
   E. apocrine gland

16. The glands that lie next to the thyroid gland and secrete a hormone that regulates the balance of calcium in the body are called the
   A. Bartholin glands
   B. pituitary glands
   C. adrenal glands
   D. parathyroid glands
   E. apocrine glands

17. The vagina is also referred to as the
   A. oviduct
   B. ovum
   C. birth canal
   D. perineum
   E. vulva

18. The large gland that secretes about 30% of the fluid part of semen is the
   A. prostate
   B. glans
   C. ductus deferens
   D. seminal vesicle
   E. penis

19. The pouch that houses the testicles is called the
    A. prostate
    B. vas deferens
    C. spermatazoa
    D. scrotum
    E. vulva

20. The ureter connects the bladder to the
    A. nephron
    B. kidney
    C. urethra
    D. meatus
    E. prostate

21. The organs that remove toxic waste products, such as urea, as well as excess water and inorganic salts are called
    A. kidneys
    B. lungs
    C. ureters
    D. glands
    E. adrenals

22. A small organ immediately behind the prostate that serves as a conduit and reservoir for sperm cells and is the place where the sperm cells mature is the
    A. vas deferens
    B. seminal vesicle
    C. epididymis
    D. prostate
    E. Cowper glands

23. Paresis means
    A. pain
    B. difficulty
    C. weakness
    D. paralysis
    E. feeling

24. The prefix "hemo" means
 A. around
 B. half
 C. under
 D. blood
 E. tube or blood vessel

25. The suffix "ostomy" means
 A. forming an opening
 B. disease
 C. tumor
 D. fear
 E. enlargement of

26. In relation to the elbow, the wrist could be described as being
 A. superior
 B. proximal
 C. medial
 D. lateral
 E. distal

27. Ventral is
 A. toward the head
 B. toward the foot
 C. toward the back
 D. toward the front
 E. toward the side

28. Which of the following abdominal organs is NOT a hollow organ?
 A. Stomach
 B. Spleen
 C. Small intestine
 D. Bladder
 E. Gall bladder

29. Because it secretes renin, the kidney plays an important part in the maintenance of
   A. temperature
   B. blood detoxification and filtration
   C. pH
   D. blood pressure
   E. hematocrit

30. Leukocytes
   A. are named because of their shape
   B. are responsible for clotting
   C. are found in the RBCs
   D. serve a defensive function
   E. all of the above

31. Which part of the autonomic nervous system governs the body's fight-or-flight reactions and stimulates cardiac activity?
   A. Pituitary
   B. Somatic nervous system
   C. Sympathetic nervous system
   D. Parasympathetic nervous system
   E. Limbic system

32. What region of the brain is responsible for the automatic responses such as respirations, cardiac function, and blood vessel control?
   A. Pituitary
   B. Medulla oblongata
   C. Cerebellum
   D. Cerebrum
   E. Limbic system

33. An ecchymosis over the mastoid bone is called
   A. Battle's sign
   B. raccoon eyes
   C. Cheyne–Stokes sign
   D. hemoptysis
   E. Grey Turner's sign

34. If the cheekbone is broken, which bone is fractured?
   A. Vomer
   B. Mandible
   C. Frontal bone
   D. Zygoma
   E. Maxilla

35. Which of the body's systems exerts control through the secretion of hormones?
   A. Endocrine
   B. Urinary
   C. Digestive
   D. Respiratory
   E. Limbic

36. The prefix "arthro" refers to the
   A. skull
   B. joint
   C. neck
   D. brain
   E. bone

37. What is the meaning of the suffix "algia"?
   A. Disease of
   B. Of a joint
   C. Pain in
   D. Disordered or difficult
   E. Enlargement of

38. All of the arteries in the body carry oxygenated blood except the
   A. aorta
   B. subclavian
   C. coronary
   D. pulmonary
   E. mitral

39. What is the meaning of the suffix "megaly"?
- **A.** Enlargement of
- **B.** Disturbance of or difficulty with
- **C.** Disease of
- **D.** Paralysis of
- **E.** Surgical removal of

40. What is the meaning of the suffix "ostomy"?
- **A.** Fear
- **B.** Forming an opening
- **C.** Tumor
- **D.** disease
- **E.** Incision into

41. Which prefix means "more than" or "excessive"?
- **A.** Ante
- **B.** Post
- **C.** Hypo
- **D.** Retro
- **E.** Hyper

42. In relation to the knee, the ankle is
- **A.** distal
- **B.** proximal
- **C.** medial
- **D.** superior
- **E.** lateral

43. The most dependable location for taking a pulse is the
- **A.** cephalic artery
- **B.** radial artery
- **C.** femoral artery
- **D.** brachial artery
- **E.** popliteal artery

QUESTIONS 44–46: For each numbered item, select the most closely related lettered item.

44. Match each phrase with the correct muscle type
    1. _____ Automaticity
    2. _____ Digestive tract, bronchi
    3. _____ Voluntary

    A. Smooth muscle
    B. Cardiac muscle
    C. Skeletal muscle

45. Match the description with the correct term.
    1. _____ Thyroid cartilage
    2. _____ Arytenoid cartilage
    3. _____ Cricoid cartilage

    A. Attached to the vocal cords
    B. Most inferior cartilage
    C. Forms Adam's apple

46. Match the hormone with the endocrine organ that secretes it.
    1. _____ Hormones regulating the other endocrine organs
    2. _____ Female sex hormones
    3. _____ Male sex hormones
    4. _____ Epinephrine
    5. _____ Hormone regulating metabolic rate
    6. _____ Insulin

    A. Adrenal
    B. Pancreas
    C. Ovary
    D. Thyroid
    E. Testes
    F. Pituitary

47. Which area of the spine describes the following phrases?
1. _____ Neck
2. _____ Fused to the pelvis
3. _____ Lower back
4. _____ Tailbone

A. Thoracic spine
B. Sacrum
C. Lumbar spine
D. Cervical spine
E. Coccyx

48. Match the phrases with the proper bone.
1. _____ On the thumb side of the forearm
2. _____ Articulates with the scapula
3. _____ Largest bone in the body
4. _____ Shinbone
5. _____ Bone in the upper arm

A. Radius
B. Femur
C. Humerus
D. Ulna
E. Fibula
F. Tibia

Explanatory Answers

1. C. Smooth muscle is found in the GI tract and bronchi. Striated or skeletal muscle is the muscle used for voluntary movement. Cardiac muscle is found only in the heart. (Ref. Caroline, p. 25)

2. A. This is the definition of stroke volume. (Ref. Caroline, p. 636)

3. D. Stroke volume is for the heart. Tidal volume is for the lungs. (Ref. Caroline, p. 638)

4. B. This is also called the brainstem. The medulla controls the automatic responses. (Ref. Caroline, pp. 28–29)

5. C. Cardiac output is rate × volume. (Ref. Caroline, p. 600)

6. B. The feeling of shortness of breath or dyspnea is one of the more important indicators of respiratory insufficiency. (Ref. Caroline, p. 179)

7. C. Diaphoresis is profuse sweating, the infamous "cold sweats." There are other causes of sweating, including overdoses of some drugs and certain mushrooms and, of course, heat exposure. (Ref. Caroline, p. 606)

8. E. Osmotic pressure is the force by which a solvent (water) moves across a semipermeable membrane from an area of higher concentration to an area of lower concentration of water, resulting in equilibration of concentrations. (Ref. Caroline, p. 60)

9. B. Diffusion is the passage of fluid and chemicals across a selectively permeable membrane. Hyperhydriosis is too much sweating, homeostasis is maintenance of stability in the body, and hycosamine is a drug similar to atropine. (Ref. Caroline, pp. 60–63)

10. A. Osmosis is the passage of water from an area of lower solute concentration to an area of higher solute concentration across a selectively permeable membrane. See comment for question 9. (Ref. Caroline, pp. 60–63)

11. C. Lymph is an almost colorless fluid that circulates in the lymphatic system. (Ref. Caroline, p. 72)

12. D. Plasma is the portion of blood from which cells have been removed. (Ref. Caroline, p. 72)

13. B. The lower chambers of the heart are the ventricles. (Ref. Caroline, p. 31)

14. E. The adrenal gland produces epinephrine, which creates part of the sympathetic fight-or-flight reaction. (Ref. Caroline, p. 113)

15. C. The thyroid is the general regulating gland for the metabolic rate. (Ref. Caroline, p. 38)

16. D. Parathyroid hormone stimulates reabsorption of calcium and metabolism of phosphorus. The parathyroids lie next to the thyroid gland. (Ref. Caroline, p. 38)

17. C. The vagina is commonly referred to as the birth canal because of its purpose in childbearing. Vulva and perineum are other names for the external female genitalia and the area between genitalia and anus, respectively. The ovum is the egg. There is no oviduct in humans. (Ref. Caroline, pp. 482, 641)

18. A. The prostate gland surrounds the urethra as it enters the bladder. It contributes about 30–40% of the fluid part of semen. It often enlarges with age and may cause urinary obstructive symptoms. Seminal vesicles store sperm and seminal fluid for ejaculations, but actually contribute little in the amount of secretions. (Ref. Caroline, p. 37)

19. D. The scrotum is a cutaneous outpouching of the abdomen that is the supporting structure of the testes. The female analogue to this structure is the vulva. (Ref. Caroline, p. 37)

20. B. The *ureter* connects the kidney to the bladder. The urethra connects the bladder to the external world through the meatus. (Ref. Caroline, p. 36)

21. A. The kidney, of course, removes water, salt, and toxic waste products. (Ref. Caroline, p. 36)

22. C. The seminal vesicles store the sperm between ejaculations and allow the sperm to mature. The vas deferens conducts the sperm from testicles to the seminal vesicle, whereas the epididymis, prostate, and Cowper glands all contribute secretions to the semen. (Ref. Caroline, p. 37)

23. C. Paresis means weakness, not paralysis (although I guess paralysis is the ultimate weakness). (Ref. Caroline, p. 15)

24. D. "Hemo" as in hemoglobin, means related to blood or blood products. (Ref. Caroline, p. 14)

25. A. The suffix "ostomy," as in tracheostomy or colostomy, means an artificially made opening. (Ref. Caroline, p. 15)

26. E. The wrist is further down the arm than the elbow and, hence, is distal to the elbow. (Ref. Caroline, p. 17)

27. D. Ventral is the old-fashioned name for anterior or toward the front of the body and dorsal, for the rear. More often we hear anterior and posterior, but some of our older colleagues still use ventral and dorsal. (Ref. Caroline, p. 17)

28. B. The spleen is a solid organ composed of very fibrous material and thus can be easily damaged by blunt trauma. Because it is very vascular, bleeding from the spleen can be quite serious. (Ref. Caroline, p. 457)

29. D. Renin is a hormone that is integral to blood pressure maintenance. The kidney also plays an important part in maintenance of blood pH, detoxification, and filtration, and, by the secretion of erythropoietin, influences the hematocrit. (Ref. Caroline, p. 42)

30. D. White blood cells, or leukocytes as they are also called, defend the body against infection. (Ref. Caroline, p. 73)

31. C. The definition of sympathetic stimulation is a fight-or-flight reaction, named from Dr. Cannon's original description of the sympathetic system. (Ref. Caroline, p. 112)

32. B. This part of the brain is also called the brainstem. The medulla controls the automatic responses. (Ref. Caroline, p. 346)

33. A. An ecchymosis about the mastoid bone may herald a basilar skull fracture, which is why Battle's sign is important. (Ref. Caroline, p. 352)

34. E. The zygoma, or more properly the zygomatic arch, forms the lateral part of the face and supports the cheeks. The maxilla, below it, is the cheekbone proper. (Ref. Caroline, p. 25)

35. A. The endocrine system acts by "remote control," exerting its effects through the secretion of such hormones as insulin and thyroid hormone. (Ref. Caroline, p. 38)

36. B. "Arthro" refers to the joint, as in arthralgia. (Ref. Caroline, p. 14)

37. C. The suffix "algia" means pain, as in neuralgia. (Ref. Caroline p. 14)

38. D. The pulmonary system carries deoxygenated blood from the heart to the lungs and then returns oxygenated blood from the lungs to the heart. (Ref. Caroline, p. 252)

39. A. The suffix "megaly" implies enlargement of, hepatomegaly, enlargement of the liver. (Ref. Caroline, p. 15)

40. B. The suffix "otomy"' means an incision into, as in tracheotomy. "Ostomy" means an opening. Beginners often confuse these two quite similar suffixes. (Ref. Caroline, p. 15)

41. E. "Hyper" means more than or excessive, as in hyperosmolar, higher than normal concentration. (Ref. Caroline, p. 14)

42. A. The ankle is further away from the heart and hence, is distal to the knee. (Ref. Caroline, p. 17)

43. C. The general rule of thumb is that the larger the artery, the more easily the pulse is felt when the patient is hypotensive. Some authors believe that a pulse can be felt in the femoral artery if the blood pressure is about 60 mm Hg or higher, but this claim has recently been disputed. It remains a good guideline that if any pulse can be felt, it will be felt first in the femoral artery. (Ref. Caroline, p. 51)

44. 1—B, 2—A, 3—C. Smooth muscle is found in the digestive tract, automaticity is associated with cardiac muscle, and skeletal muscle is under voluntary control. (Ref. Caroline, p. 25)

45. 1—C, 2—A, 3—B. (Ref. Caroline, p. 169)

46. 1—F, 2—C, 3—E, 4—A, 5—D, 6—B.

47. 1—D, 2—B, 3—C, 4—B.

48. 1—A, 2—C, 3—B, 4—F, 5—C.

2 Patient Assessment, Communication Skills, and Legal Questions

---

QUESTIONS 49–71: Select the ONE most appropriate answer.

---

49. What is the appropriate order for presenting the following medical information?
1. History of present illness
2. Past medical history
3. Chief complaint
4. Physical examination
5. Age and sex
6. Treatment
   - **A.** 3,1,5,2,4,6
   - **B.** 3,4,1,5,2,6
   - **C.** 5,3,1,2,4,6
   - **D.** 3,5,2,1,4,6
   - **E.** 5,3,6,1,4,2

50. Which is not a symptom?
   - **A.** Dizziness
   - **B.** Nausea
   - **C.** Dyspnea
   - **D.** Ecchymosis
   - **E.** Anorexia

51. In examination of a patient complaining of abdominal pain,
    A. the quadrant of pain should be palpated before the other quadrants.
    B. the different quadrants can be palpated in any order.
    C. the quadrant of pain should be palpated after the other quadrants.
    D. the quadrant of pain should not be palpated.
    E. None of the above.

52. Rales are
    A. abnormal heart sounds
    B. easily heard without a stethoscope
    C. sounds caused by fluid in the alveoli or interstitial spaces
    D. unimportant for determining prehospital care
    E. sounds heard in the upper abdominal quadrants

53. Which sign is most likely to be found with early pulmonary edema?
    A. Wheezes
    B. Absent breath sounds
    C. Crackles or rales
    D. Stridor
    E. Prolonged expiratory phase

54. During a field exam, which would be considered inappropriate?
    A. Auscultation of the chest
    B. Determining pupillary size and reactivity to light
    C. Testing response by nipple pinching
    D. Testing for pain response by sternal pressure
    E. Observing respirations

55. Indiscriminate use of sirens should be avoided
    A. in transporting patients with chest pain and shortness of breath
    B. enroute to a call with a reported bridge jumper
    C. whenever the nature of the call is unknown
    D. in all of the preceding situations
    E. A and B only

56. Which of the following is NOT usually considered a high priority of field emergency medicine?
   A. Diagnosis
   B. Intervention
   C. Data collection
   D. Manual skills
   E. Reporting

57. Which of the following is NOT usually a function or responsibility of the paramedic?
   A. Prompt and efficient care of the patient before transfer to the hospital
   B. Control of the accident scene
   C. Orderly transfer of the patient to the hospital
   D. Transfer of information obtained to the hospital
   E. Decision to pronounce the patient dead

58. In the United States an ambulance is customarily identified by
   A. red and blue warning lights
   B. a Red Cross
   C. the word AMBULANCE written in reverse on the rear door or bumper
   D. the Star of Life
   E. the red and white colors of the body of the ambulance

59. Which criterion must be fulfilled to prove negligence?
   A. The EMT had a duty to act.
   B. There was a lack in the standard of care.
   C. The victim suffered an injury.
   D. The victim's injury resulted from or was made worse by action or lack of action on the part of an EMT.
   E. All of the above.

60. The primary reason for drug legislation (such as the Federal Food, Drug & Cosmetic Act) is to
  A. keep doctors and health professionals from abusing drugs themselves
  B. ensure the safety of drugs manufactured
  C. control narcotic drugs
  D. ensure the sterility of manufactured goods
  E. administer vaccinations to children

61. The Good Samaritan law is intended to
  A. establish the liability of providers of inadequate care for accident victims
  B. punish people who do not stop and render aid at an accident
  C. protect victims of accidents from incompetent first aid treatments
  D. protect those who render appropriate aid at accident scenes from prosecution
  E. ensure that all providers have adequate skills to render proper first aid

62. Which is abandonment?
  A. Leaving one patient to care for another at the scene of a multivictim accident
  B. Leaving the scene after initiating patient care
  C. The patient demands to be left alone
  D. The responder is not able to provide care
  E. None of the above

63. Once you stop at an accident, if you leave or fail to pass on care to someone at least as well trained as yourself, you may be liable for legal action under the
  A. principle of abandonment
  B. Good Samaritan Act
  C. medical malpractice act
  D. medical malfeasance act
  E. implied consent principle

64. A paramedic may be held liable for
  A. waiting for parental consent to treat a minor with serious injuries
  B. not providing care to an overdose patient who refuses care
  C. administering basic drugs to restart the heart of a patient in cardiac arrest without standing orders or contact with the base physician
  D. performing an open thoracotomy or an amputation
  E. all of the above

65. To prove negligence on the part of a paramedic, the court must find all but ONE of the following:
  A. The paramedic had a duty to act.
  B. The standard of care was not met.
  C. By the paramedic's action or inaction, an injury was sustained.
  D. The patient suffered because of the injury.
  E. The paramedic was reimbursed for his/her time.

66. You decide to aid an injured person, but receive a call for a cardiac arrest. You decide to leave before help arrives. You may be found liable
  A. for abandonment
  B. for neglect
  C. for desertion
  D. only if potentially fatal injuries are present in the first victim
  E. for malfeasance

67. The minimal accepted care based upon local protocols, court decisions, and both local and nationwide professional standards is known as the
  A. duty to act
  B. critical care code
  C. federal protocol standard
  D. standard of care
  E. ASTM protocol

68. An ambulance with a conventional truck cab—chassis with a modular ambulance body is known as a
   A. type I ambulance
   B. type II ambulance
   C. type III ambulance
   D. type IV ambulance

69. The record of care you render to a patient (trip sheet) should be complete, should contain patient information and your observations, and is
   A. a legal document
   B. later filed as public record
   C. the property of the receiving hospital
   D. a portion of the patient's records

70. What is the most appropriate order of priorities when responding to the scene of a three-car accident?
   A. Safety, significant information, outside help
   B. Communications with base, obtaining outside help, triage
   C. Primary survey, secondary survey, obtaining outside help
   D. Safety, primary survey, immediate intervention, transport
   E. Primary survey, secondary survey, intervention, transport

71. What is the proper order for doing a primary survey (initial exam for life-threatening problems)?
   A. Check for airway, breathing, pulse, and bleeding
   B. Check for pulse, exsanguinating hemorrhage, and breathing
   C. Check for level of consciousness, pulse, breathing, and blood pressure
   D. Check for exsanguinating bleeding, breathing, and pulse
   E. Contact dispatch for help, initiate ABCs, and transport rapidly

Explanatory Answers

49. C. The format of a medical report is standardized so that you do not forget important details and so that each party knows what to expect next in the report. (Ref. Caroline, p. 53)

50. D. Symptoms are those things that the patient reports as part of the history. A sign is something that the medical examiner notes to be visible, audible, or palpable. Therefore, ecchymosis is a sign not a symptom. (Ref. Caroline, p. 634)

51. C. A gentle examiner will deliberately hurt the patient last, so that the patient will not guard and make the rest of the exam more difficult. Extensive examination of an abdominal pain in the field serves only to ensure that the patient guards and has a more difficult time with subsequent examinations. (Ref. Caroline, p. 458)

52. C. Rales, sometimes called crackles, are important indicators of fluid in the alveoli or interstitial spaces. They tend to sound like the often advertised "Rice Krispies." Although severe rales may occasionally be heard without the stethoscope, usually careful auscultation is necessary. (Ref. Caroline, pp. 632, 269)

53. C. Crackles, or rales, are most often found with early pulmonary edema. Wheezes are a less frequent but important finding in pulmonary edema, eg, "cardiac asthma." (Ref. Caroline, p. 269)

54. C. This is not considered good form in the field, especially on female patients. (Ref. Caroline, pp. 43–48)

55. E. For psychiatric patients and for those whose physical condition would be worsened by stress, lights and sirens should not be used if possible. (Ref. Caroline, p. 268)

56. A. The purpose of field medicine is the intervention in the patient's condition by collection of data, application of manual skills, and reporting to the emergency physician what has been seen in the field as well as any treatment or intervention of cause of the illness or injury. (Ref. Caroline, p. 3)

57. E. It is the responsibility of the EMT or paramedic to care for the sick and injured patient both before transportation and enroute to the hospital and to deliver information about the patient to the hospital staff; control of the accident scene is usually left to the police or fire department; however, if no one else is around the scene, the EMT is ultimately responsible for that task as well. The prudent EMT elicits orders from the base physician as to pronouncing a patient dead after reporting findings on the scene regarding the patient's condition.

58. D. The Star of Life is a federal standard for identification of ambulances and should be prominently displayed on front, back, and both sides. (Ref. Grant, p. 18; AAOS, p. 515)

59. E. The classic components of a malpractice action are (1) a duty to act, (2) a deficit in care, (3) an injury to the patient, and (4) evidence that the deficit in care caused the injury. (Ref. ACLS, p. 271)

60. B. Actually, the Bureau of Narcotics and Dangerous Drugs (BNDD) wages the war on drugs. FDA is responsible for ensurance of the safety and efficacy of drugs. (Ref. Caroline, p. 105)

61. D. The Good Samaritan laws are designed to protect those who stop and render aid to ill and injured folks. These laws generally do not apply to EMTs, paramedics, nurses, and physicians who are part of paid emergency response crews during their paid time. Such providers are usually protected when they are off duty, however. The laws concerning unpaid volunteers are often ambiguous. (Ref. AAOS, p. 18; Grant, p. 16)

62. B. Abandonment is leaving your patient. When you have more than one patient, it is appropriate to ensure that all are triaged and that care is rendered to the most critically injured, SALVAGEABLE patient. (Ref. Brady, p. 14; AAOS, p. 16)

63. A. Interestingly, you do not have to stop to provide care, but if you do stop, you may not abandon the patient unless you hand the patient to someone able to administer an equal or higher level of care. (This means that even a physician should ride with the patient to the emergency department.) (Ref. Grant, p. 14; AAOS, p. 16)

64. E. Whenever a paramedic acts outside of established protocols, legal action is likely. When the patient does not receive appropriate care, legal action is just as likely. Not caring for a patient is often viewed by the legal community as more trouble than acting and making a mistake. The general rule of thumb is that you should always consider what is most appropriate for the patient.

65. E. In a suit for malpractice, the volunteer is as liable as the paid paramedic. (Ref. Grant, p. 14; AAOS, p. 15)

66. A. This is a classic case of abandonment. Once a paramedic starts to give care, he or she may leave only when the patient has been properly cared for by protocol or the patient has been turned over to someone able to give an equal or higher level of care. (Ref. Grant, p. 14; AAOS, p. 16)

67. D. The standard of care is the published acceptable means and methods of caring for the patient. This standard is often not well codified, and may be found in multiple places (often differing in content). It is this "difference of opinion" that makes and breaks some malpractice trials. In some cases, the decision is easy, such as spinal immobilization for all cervical spine fractures. In other cases, such as which drugs to use for what conditions, the "standard" is not so explicit nor standardized and often differs substantially from community to community.

68. A. The type I ambulance is often chosen because the truck chassis can be readily replaced when it wears out, and the expensive module can be reused. (Ref. Brady, p. 18; AAOS, p. 516)

69. A. Although the trip sheet may be left with the hospital to be incorporated into the medical records, and is often a public record, it may not be in all localities. In all places, however, it is a legal record. (Ref. Brady, p. 16; AAOS, p. 550)

70. A. The most important consideration in rescue work should be the safety of the rescuer. It is more difficult for the next crew to arrive on the scene if they must rescue the first rescuers. It is likewise difficult on the rescuers who become victims. Following safety, you need to determine the nature of the incident, the number of victims, and the estimated severity of their injuries to ask for appropriate help. (Ref. Abbott, p. 17; Caroline, p. 582)

71. A. As always, the first things that you should check are the ABCs of medicine—airway, breathing, and circulation. (Ref. Caroline, p. 43)

3 Shock

General

72. A requirement of normal tissue perfusion is
    A. adequate blood and plasma volume
    B. a properly functioning heart
    C. an intact vascular system that can vary the resistance to blood flow
    D. all of the above
    E. A and B only

73. The hematocrit is
    A. ratio of hemoglobin concentration to number of red blood cells
    B. ratio of leukocytes to erythrocytes and platelets
    C. volume of hemoglobin per unit of circulating blood
    D. percentage of packed red blood cells in a given volume of blood
    E. number of units of blood

74. The universal blood donor type is
    A. A
    B. B
    C. AB
    D. O
    E. E

27

75. The type of shock resulting most often from internal or external hemorrhage is
    A. neurogenic
    B. cardiogenic
    C. hypovolemic
    D. anaphylactic
    E. metabolic

76. Which of the following would be considered adequate management of hypovolemic shock?
    A. Oxygen
    B. KVO IV D$_5$W
    C. Foley catheter
    D. Cardiac monitor
    E. None of the above

77. Which of the following best defines shock?
    A. Systolic pressure less than 90 mm Hg
    B. Loss of consciousness
    C. Increased vascular flow
    D. Inadequate tissue perfusion
    E. Pulse greater than 120

78. Sunken eyes, postural hypotension, and dry mucous membranes are associated with
    A. overhydration
    B. dehydration
    C. sodium bicarbonate deficit
    D. sodium bicarbonate excess
    E. overdose of atropine

79. Packed cells are indicated when
    A. the patient rapidly needs increased oxygen-transporting capacity
    B. the patient has severe anemia
    C. the extra volume of whole blood would be an added burden for the body to circulate
    D. the other components of the blood are needed for another patient
    E. all of the above

Military Antishock Trousers

80. Military Antishock trousers (MAST)
    A. cannot be used if CPR will need to be performed
    B. should be removed as soon as the blood pressure returns to normal
    C. are contraindicated in cardiac arrest
    D. are applied so that the upper edge is just below the rib cage
    E. cannot be used on pregnant women

81. How are MAST deflated?
    A. Left leg chamber first
    B. Right leg chamber first
    C. Abdominal compartment first
    D. Both leg chambers first
    E. All sections simultaneously deflated, but only after examination by a physician

82. An absolute CONTRAindication to the use of MAST is
    A. hypovolemic shock
    B. head injury
    C. pulmonary edema
    D. penetrating abdominal injury
    E. all of the above

83. Which is a field indication for deflation of MAST?
    A. Diaphragmatic rupture
    B. Cerebral edema
    C. Cardiopulmonary arrest
    D. Pulmonary edema
    E. Pregnancy

Explanatory Answers

72. D. The three requirements of tissue perfusion are fluid, pump, and plumbing. (Ref. Caroline, pp. 78–79)

73. D. Hematocrit is the percentage of blood composed of red blood cells. (Ref. Caroline, p. 72)

74. D. Type O blood is considered the "universal" donor, and in major trauma with extensive bleeding, we often give un-cross-matched type O blood. Even type O blood has incompatibilities among the "minor" blood types, so this practice is avoided if at all possible. (Ref. Caroline, p. 74, Table 3-2)

75. C. Hypovolemic shock occurs from low blood volume. Hemorrhage is a cause of low blood volume, as is fluid loss from vomiting and diarrhea. (Ref. Caroline, p. 79, Table 3-4)

76. E. Hypovolemic shock requires fluid replacement. Therefore, a keep-vein-open (KVO) infusion of D_5W would be not only inadequate but negligent treatment of the hypovolemic patient. Likewise, all of the other procedures are appropriate, but not sufficient management for the patient with hypovolemic shock. (Ref. Caroline, p. 81; Abbott, pp. 64–67)

77. D. Shock is defined as a decrease in tissue perfusion, but is often thought of as a low blood pressure. This is a fallacy. The elderly patient with a blood pressure that usually is about 190 systolic may be frankly shocky at a blood pressure of 120 systolic! Likewise, the small child may have entirely normal perfusion with a blood pressure of 85 systolic. The healthy well-conditioned adult will attempt to maintain the blood pressure by vasoconstriction, and will be able to keep a blood pressure of about 110–120 systolic, despite the loss of as much as 1–1.5 L of blood. This patient may be in shock, despite a normal blood pressure. (Ref. Caroline, p. 79)

78. B. All of the symptoms listed are associated with dehydration. Atropine overdose would be expected to produce dry mucous membranes, but would not produce sunken eyes or postural hypotension. Sodium bicarbonate changes would produce a change in blood pH. (Ref. Caroline, p. 78; Abbott, pp. 66–67)

79. E. Actually, packing the red cells (squeezing out the fluid components of the blood) leaves the fluid components available for use in other patients. Either packed blood cells or whole blood provides increased oxygen-transporting capacity and is used to treat severe anemia. (Ref. Caroline, pp. 74, 75)

80. D. Military antishock trousers (MAST) are applied so that the upper edge does not obstruct respirations. If used in pregnancy, the abdominal section should not be inflated. MAST should not be removed until the patient has been stabilized with intravenous fluids and should almost never be removed quickly. (Ref. Caroline, pp. 89–92; Abbott, pp. 174–175)

81. C. The abdominal compartment should be deflated first so that MAST do not act as a tourniquet at the waist! (Ref. Caroline, p. 92)

82. C. MAST can be used without the abdominal compartment inflated for patients with a suspected abdominal injury. Head injury is not an absolute contraindication, particularly if combined with hypovolemic shock. On the other hand, pulmonary edema is an absolute contraindication. (Ref. Caroline, p. 90; Abbott, pp. 174–175)

83. D. Diaphragmatic rupture, cerebral edema, and pregnancy should alert you to consider not applying MAST. It is unlikely, however, that these conditions would cause you to deflate them, once applied. Development of pulmonary edema should cause you to deflate MAST! (Ref. BTLS, p. 177; Abbott, p. 174)

4 Intravenous Therapy

QUESTIONS 84–99: Select the ONE most appropriate answer.

84. The major hazard involved in employing a catheter-through-needle system is
    A. infection
    B. hematoma
    C. catheter embolus
    D. extravasation of the infused fluid
    E. low flow rate through the catheter

85. A solution with a concentration of solute molecules equivalent to that inside the cells (eg, normal saline) is said to be
    A. hypotonic
    B. isotonic
    C. hypertonic
    D. colloidal
    E. orthotonic

86. What size catheter should be used for volume expansion?
    A. 16 gauge, 20 cm long
    B. 14 gauge, 5 cm long
    C. 20 gauge, 3 cm long
    D. 18 gauge, 5 cm long
    E. 22 gauge, 1.5 cm long

87. Plasma constitutes what percentage of blood volume in the normal patient?
A. 35
B. 45
C. 55
D. 65
E. 75

88. Protein solutions are classified as
A. crystalloids
B. electrolytes
C. diuretics
D. colloids
E. none of the above

89. The major extracellular cation is
A. Na^+
B. Ca^{2+}
C. K^+
D. Cl^-
E. HCO_3^-

90. When placed in a hypertonic fluid, cells
A. shrink
B. swell
C. remain unchanged
D. explode
E. lyse

91. The physician orders an infusion of 1 L (1,000 mL) of normal saline in 4 hours. The administration set being used provides 10 drops/mL. What infusion should be set for
A. 15 drops/min
B. 100 drops/min
C. 840 drops/min
D. 42 drops/min
E. 60 drops/min

92. The physician orders 300 in 3 hours via an administration
    set that delivers 60 drops/mL. How fast should the solution
    run?
    A. 15 drops/min
    B. 100 drops/min
    C. 60 drops/min
    D. 120 drops/min
    E. 90 drops/min

93. What percentage of an adult's body weight is water?
    A. 30
    B. 40
    C. 50
    D. 60
    E. 80

94. What percentage of total body weight is extracellular fluid?
    A. 5
    B. 15
    C. 30
    D. 60
    E. 80

95. What is interstitial fluid?
    1. The water bathing the cells
    2. The water within the blood vessels
    3. The water inside the cell
    4. Part of the water outside the cells
       A. 2 and 4
       B. 3 and 4
       C. 1, 2, and 4
       D. 2, 3, and 4
       E. All of the above

96. What is intravascular fluid (plasma)?
    1. The part of the fluid outside of the cells
    2. The fluid within the blood vessels
    3. The fluid bathing the cells
    4. The fluid inside the cells
        A. 2 and 4
        B. 3 and 4
        C. 1 and 2
        D. 1, 2, and 3
        E. All of the above

97. In starting an IV, the tourniquet is used to obstruct
    A. arterial and venous flow
    B. arterial flow
    C. venous flow
    D. capillary flow
    E. lymph flow

98. Which bag will infuse faster?
    A. 400 cc of a solution of packed cells diluted 50/50 with saline
    B. 200 cc of packed cells

99. Through which configuration will a solution infuse faster?
    A. 16-gauge, 1½-inch-long antecubital intravenous needle
    B. 16-gauge, 6-inch-long subclavian catheter
    C. 16-gauge, 8-inch-long femoral line
    D. 18-gauge, 24-inch-long brachial CVP line
    E. 7-French, triple-lumen CVP line

QUESTIONS 100–102: Fill in the appropriate words or phrases.

---

100. State four reasons for starting an IV in an emergency.
    1. _____
    2. _____
    3. _____
    4. _____

101. What are four local complications of IV therapy?
  1. _____
  2. _____
  3. _____
  4. _____

102. What are four systemic complications of IV therapy?
  1. _____
  2. _____
  3. _____
  4. _____

103. Name four peripheral veins.
  1. _____
  2. _____
  3. _____
  4. _____

QUESTION 104: Fill in the appropriate numbers, from 1 to 8.

---

104. What is the proper sequence for starting an IV in the external jugular vein?
  1. _____ Cleanse and anesthetize the skin.
  2. _____ Puncture the skin with the bevel of the needle upward; enter the vein from the top or the side.
  3. _____ Note blood return and advance the cannula.
  4. _____ Align the cannula in the direction of the vein with the point aimed toward the same shoulder.
  5. _____ Tourniquet the vein with a finger.
  6. _____ Place the patient in a supine, head-down position.
  7. _____ Withdraw the needle and attach the tubing.
  8. _____ Dress the IV site.

Explanatory Answers

84. C. Shearing off the end of the catheter with the needle tip if the catheter is withdrawn through the needle is a real hazard. The end can then become a "needle embolus" and head to the heart via the venous circulation. (Ref. Caroline, p. 89)

85. B. Again, a solution isotonic to the cell has a concentration of molecules equal to that inside the cell. (Ref. Caroline, pp. 60–62)

86. B. Resistance to flow increases with increasing catheter length and decreasing catheter size. For fluid resuscitation, the shortest, fattest catheter should be used, the 14-gauge, 5-cm-long catheter. (Ref. ACLS p. 141; Abbott p. 223)

87. C. The fluid components of the blood (plasma) constitute about half of the blood volume of the normal human. (Ref. Caroline, p. 72)

88. D. Proteins in solution are colloids, crystalloids have crystals (salts) in solution. Hence plasma would be a colloid, and normal saline solution a crystalloid. (Ref. Caroline, pp. 63, 75)

89. A. Cations are positive; anions are negative. The principal cation in the body is sodium, Na^+. (Ref. Caroline, p. 63)

90. A. When cells are placed in a hypertonic solution, fluids leave the cell, causing it to shrink. In the extreme case this may be termed *crenation*. (Ref. Caroline, pp. 62–63)

91. D. Drops per minute $= \dfrac{\text{(volume infused} \times \text{drops/mL)}}{\text{(time of infusion in minutes)}}$.
(Ref. Caroline, p. 87)

92. B. Drops per minute $= \dfrac{\text{(volume infused} \times \text{drops/mL)}}{\text{(time of infusion in minutes)}}$.
(Ref. Caroline, p. 87)

93. D. In the average human, under ideal conditions, total body water constitutes about 60% of the body weight. (Ref. Caroline, p. 58)

94. B. In the average human, under ideal conditions, about 15% of the body is extracellular fluid, the spinal fluids, the water bathing the cells, and the blood in the blood vessels. (Ref. Caroline, p. 58)

95. C. The interstitial fluids are cerebrospinal fluid, intraocular fluid, and the fluid bathing the cells—the lymph. (Ref. Caroline, p. 58)

96. D. Intravascular fluid is the water component of the blood. It is only part of the extracellular fluids. (Ref. Caroline, p. 58)

97. C. In cases of bleeding, the tourniquet is used to obstruct arterial flow, but in starting an IV or drawing blood, the tourniquet should be used to obstruct venous flow and dilate the vein. (Ref. Caroline, p. 84; Abbott, p. 183)

98. A. Packed red blood cells are made by removing most of the plasma from the blood ("packing" it). The resultant solution has more red blood cells (higher hematocrit) and hence is much more viscous than whole blood. The red blood cells can be reconstituted by adding saline to the bag. The resultant solution actually is less viscous than whole blood, because many of the plasma proteins are missing. The greater viscosity of the packed red blood cells makes them flow much more slowly than the reconstituted cells. (Ref. Caroline, p. 74)

99. A. Flow through a catheter depends on the diameter and length of the catheter. Flow is much faster through a short, wide-bore catheter than through a long, narrow-gauge catheter. As flow rates are of concern in trauma, this is not a trivial point. The only short fat needle mentioned is the antecubital 16-gauge needle. The 7-French, triple-lumen catheter has a larger outside diameter, but is effectively three smaller tubes that are longer than the antecubital. (Ref. BTLS, p. 153; ACLS, p. 141; Abbott, p. 223)

100. Administer drugs, administer fluids, obtain blood specimens, catheterize for monitoring and pacing, IV lifeline. The intravenous line may not be necessary in every myocardial infarction. Unfortunately, we do not know which patient will require fluids, drugs, monitoring, or pacing. Hence we should start an intravenous lifeline on all patients with suspected myocardial infarction. In trauma patients, the necessity for large-volume resuscitation should mandate not one, but two large-bore intravenous lines. (Ref. ACLS, p. 141; Abbott, p. 183)

101. Hematoma, cellulitis, thrombosis, phlebitis, infusion of drugs into the tissues. Although intravenous therapy is generally safe, it is not totally benign. (Ref. ACLS, p. 143; Abbott, p. 185)

102. Sepsis, pulmonary thromboembolism, air embolism, catheter fragment embolism. Intravenous therapy, no matter what route, carries some significant systemic complications that must be avoided, if possible. (Ref. ACLS, p. 143; Abbott, p. 185)

103. Cephalic and basilic veins are found in the upper arm. Median cephalic and median basilic extend through the antecubital fossa; radial and ulnar veins extend through the forearm. The dorsal plexus is found on the dorsum of the hand. The long sapphenous is found about the medial malleolus in the lower extremity. The external jugular is found to either side of the neck. (Ref. ACLS, p. 143)

104. The proper sequence is 6,1,4,5,2,3,7,8. (Ref. ACLS, pp. 144–145)

5 Pharmacology

Select the ONE most appropriate answer.

General

105. The glass containers with rubber stoppers that are used for storage of sterile powdered or liquid drugs for parenteral use are called
    A. drips
    B. prefilled syringes
    C. vials
    D. ampules
    E. flasks

106. Chemical compounds totally dissolved in a liquid form are
    A. solutions
    B. syrups
    C. suspensions
    D. milks
    E. lotions

107. Rate of action is determined by route of administration. What is the correct order for slowest to fastest rate of action?
   A. IV, ET, IM, SQ, PO
   B. PO, SQ, ET, IM, IV
   C. PO, SQ, IM, ET, IV
   D. SQ, PO, IM, ET, IV
   E. ET, IV, SQ, IM, PO

108. Medical command has ordered you to administer 0.3 cc of aqueous epinephrine 1 : 1,000 to a patient suffering an asthma attack. What is the usual route of administration?
   A. ET
   B. IV
   C. IM
   D. PO
   E. SQ

109. Which name does a pharmaceutical company give to a drug when it is first developed, but before it is officially available?
   A. Chemical name
   B. Official name
   C. Generic name
   D. Trade name
   E. Brand name

110. If epinephrine cannot be administered intravenously during a cardiac arrest, what alternative route is preferred?
   A. SQ
   B. PO
   C. ET
   D. IP
   E. IM

111. During a cardiac arrest, intramuscular injections are not given because
    A. such injections are difficult to administer properly
    B. such injections interfere with later determination of myocardial infarction by chemical testing
    C. none of the drugs normally given during cardiac arrest can be administered intramuscularly
    D. absorption is slow and unreliable during cardiac arrest
    E. the drugs are apt to be adversely affected by the cardiac medications used during an arrest

112. Drugs that may be given intratracheally (IT) include all the following EXCEPT
    A. epinephrine
    B. sodium bicarbonate
    C. atropine
    D. lidocaine
    E. valium

Calculations

113. 50 cc of dextrose 50% =
    A. 250 g sugar
    B. 2,500 g sugar
    C. 25 g sugar
    D. 2.5 g sugar
    E. 0.25 g sugar

114. 500 cc of 5% dextrose =
    A. 2.5 g dextrose
    B. 25 g dextrose
    C. 250 g dextrose
    D. 2,500 g dextrose
    E. 125 g dextrose

115. Calcium chloride is provided as the 10% solution. If you are ordered to administer 500 mg to a patient who has ingested fluoride solution, you should give
   A. 0.5 mL
   B. 1 mL
   C. 5 mL
   D. 50 mL
   E. 12.5 mL

116. You have a 1-cc vial of atropine that contains 1 mg. Your orders are to administer 0.01 mg/kg to a patient who weighs 185 lb. How much atropine should you administer?
   A. 0.5 cc
   B. 0.8 cc
   C. 0.86 cc
   D. 1.0 cc
   E. 1.72 cc

117. Lasix is supplied in 2-mL ampules containing 20 mg. Your orders are to administer 0.7 mg/kg to a 140-lb patient. How much Lasix should you administer?
   A. 4.0 mL
   B. 4.5 mL
   C. 5.0 mL
   D. 5.5 mL
   E. 6.0 mL

118. You have been ordered to add 2 g of lidocaine to 500 mL of D_5W. When this is done, what will be the concentration of lidocaine?
   A. 1 mg/mL
   B. 2 mg/mL
   C. 3 mg/mL
   D. 4 mg/mL
   E. 6 mg/mL

119. You prepare a solution of 1 mg isoproterenol (Isuprel) in 500 mL of D_5W. What is the resulting concentration?
   A. 0.2 $\mu g/mL$
   B. 2 $\mu g/mL$
   C. 20 $\mu g/mL$
   D. 20 mg/mL
   E. 2,000 $\mu g/mL$

120. The pediatric dose of epinephrine 1 : 10,000 is 0.1 mL/kg; this is
   A. 1 mg/kg
   B. 0.1 mg/kg
   C. 0.1 mg/kg
   D. 0.001 mg/kg
   E. 0.05 mg/kg

121. You are treating a patient who has taken a medication overdose of twenty-five 30-mg tablets. What dosage of medication has she taken?
   A. 0.075 g
   B. 0.75 g
   C. 7.5 g
   D. 75 g
   E. 750 g

QUESTIONS 122–124: Calculate the conversion and fill in the appropriate amount.

---

122. Calculate the following conversions:
   1. 450 mg = _____ g
   2. 24 cc = _____ mL
   3. 6.7 cc H_2O = _____ mg H_2O
   4. 65 kg = _____ lb

123. Calculate the following conversions:
   1. 2.3 kg = _____ g
   2. 0.03 kg = _____ mg
   3. 15 g = _____ mg
   4. 84 kg = _____ lb

124. Calculate the following conversions:
1. 0.75 g/L = _____ mg/L
2. 65 mL = _____ L
3. $\frac{1}{4}$ g = _____ mg
4. 18 lb = _____ kg

QUESTIONS 125–132: Read the statement and fill in the appropriate amount.

---

125. The doctor has ordered bretylium tosylate (Bretylol), 5 mg/kg, to be given to a 110-lb patient. You have two ampules of bretylium. The glass ampule contains 500 mg of Bretylol in 20 mL. To administer the drug, each ampule needs to be diluted to 50 mL total volume. What volume must be given to the patient?
_____ cc

126. How much sodium bicarbonate should be administered to a 176-lb patient? The proper dose is 1 mEq/kg, and it comes in a 50-cc syringe containing 50 mEq. You have four prefilled syringes.
_____ mEq

127. Your patient weighs 75 kg. You have mixed 200 mg of dopamine in 250 mL of D_5W. How many drops per minute should the IV run if the dose is 8 μg/kg/min? (60 drops/min = 1 mL)
_____ drops/min

128. Your patient weighs 76 kg. Two milligrams of isoproterenol (Isuprel) have been mixed into 250 mL of D_5W. What is the rate of your IV, in drops per minute, if the dose is 6 μg/min? (60 drops/min = 1 mL)
_____ drops/min

129. Your patient, who weighs 64 kg, is to receive 5 μg/kg/min of dopamine. At a rate of 60 drops/min = 1 mL, what is the drip rate if the IV contains 400 mg of dopamine in 500 mL of D$_5$W?

_____ drops/min

130. You are ordered to administer 3 mg/min of lidocaine to your 100-kg patient. If 60 drops/min = 1 mL, what is the drip rate for an IV that contains 2 g of lidocaine in 500 mL of D$_5$W?

_____ drops/min

131. You are ordered to give 10 μg/min of Isuprel to your 90-kg patient. At a rate of 60 drops/min = 1 mL, what is the drip rate if the IV contains 4 mg isuprel in 500 mL of D$_5$W?

_____ drops/min

132. You are ordered to give your 53-kg patient 5 μg/kg/min of dopamine. At a rate of 60 drops/min = 1 mL, what is the drip rate of an IV containing 200 mg of dopamine in 250 mL of D$_5$W?

_____ drops/min

QUESTIONS 133-179: Select the ONE most appropriate answer.

Pharmacologic Agents

Atropine

133. The correct dosage of atropine for a cardiac patient is
    A. 0.5 mg IV push, repeated every 5 minutes to a total dose of 2.0 mg
    B. 5 mg IV bolus
    C. 5-7 mg/kg IV push
    D. 50 cc IV push, followed by 1-2 g in 250-500 cc D$_5$W
    E. 5 mg IV push, repeated every 5 minutes to a total dose of 20 mg

134. Effects of atropine include all EXCEPT
  A. tachycardia
  B. increased oral secretions
  C. increased intraocular pressure
  D. enhanced atrioventricular (AV) conduction
  E. urinary retention

β-Blocker Agents

135. What is propranolol?
  A. β-Stimulator
  B. β-Blocker
  C. α-Stimulator
  D. α-Blocker
  E. γ-Emitter

136. Propranolol may exacerbate effects of all of the diseases listed EXCEPT
  A. juvenile onset (insulin-dependent) diabetes
  B. hypovolemic shock
  C. asthma
  D. congestive heart failure
  E. supraventricular tachycardia

137. Because propranolol is a nonselective β-adrenergic blocker, in clinical doses it will not oppose the effects of β-adrenergic antagonists on
  A. renal vessels
  B. cardiac receptors
  C. bronchial smooth muscle
  D. vascular smooth muscle
  E. axonal cells

138. Which is not an adverse effect of propranolol?
  A. Bradycardia
  B. Hypotension
  C. Nausea or vomiting
  D. Coma
  E. Exacerbation of asthma

139. What is the drug of choice for congestive heart failure resulting from propranolol administration?
   A. Digitalis
   B. Labatelol
   C. Epinephrine
   D. Dopamine
   E. Calcium chloride

Sodium Bicarbonate

140. Sodium bicarbonate is
   A. a first-line antiarrhythmic agent
   B. useful for treating alkalosis
   C. an alkalotic agent
   D. necessary for treatment of all cardiac arrest victims
   E. never given to pregnant or pediatric patients

141. Which statement is NOT true concerning the use of sodium bicarbonate?
   A. It improves the ability to ventilate the patient.
   B. It may be helpful when treating patients with preexisting acidosis.
   C. It shifts the oxyhemoglobin saturation curve, inhibiting the release of oxygen.
   D. It may inactivate epinephrine and other catecholamines.
   E. It may cause increased osmotic pressure.

142. What is an appropriate dose of sodium bicarbonate?
   A. 1 mEq/kg initially, followed by no more than one-half of this dose every 5 minutes
   B. 2 mEq/kg initially, followed by no more than 1 mEq every 10 minutes
   C. 1 mEq/kg initially, followed by no more than one-half of this dose every 10 minutes
   D. 1–2 mEq/kg every 10 minutes
   E. 100 mEq/kg every 10 minutes

143. Sodium bicarbonate is contraindicated for
   A.   diabetic ketoacidosis
   B.   tricyclic antidepressant overdose
   C.   hypernatremia
   D.   metabolic acidosis with adequate ventilatory status
   E.   renal acidosis

Bretylium

144. What is the recommended continuous infusion rate for bretylium?
   A.   0.5–2 μg/kg/min
   B.   1–4 mg/h
   C.   30–60 mL/min
   D.   1–4 mg/min
   E.   350 mg/min

145. Which of the following conditions are adverse reactions to bretylium?
   1.   Precipitation of seizures
   2.   Increased frequency of ventricular ectopy
   3.   Orthostatic hypotension
   4.   Respiratory depression
   5.   Nausea and vomiting
      A.   1,3, and 5
      B.   2,4, and 5
      C.   3 and 5
      D.   All of the above
      E.   None of the above

146. What are the cardiovascular effects of bretylium?
   1.   Increase in ventricular fibrillation threshold
   2.   Prolongation of action potential duration in normal myocardium.
   3.   Early increase in arterial pressure and heart rate
   4.   Late hypotension
   5.   Late decrease in arterial pressure and heart rate
      A.   1,2,3, and 4
      B.   1,2,3, and 5
      C.   1,3,4, and 5
      D.   4 only
      E.   All of the above

147. What is the recommended initial dose of bretylium for refractory ventricular fibrillation?
   A. 10 mg/kg IV bolus
   B. 5 mg/kg IV bolus
   C. 350 mg IV bolus
   D. 500 mg IV bolus
   E. 5 mg/min IV drip

148. Ventricular fibrillation continues after the initial bretylium bolus and a subsequent countershock. The dosage of bretylium should be increased to
   A. 10 mg/kg IV, repeated at 15-minute intervals to a maximum of 30 mg/kg
   B. Repeat administration of bretylium is contraindicated
   C. 700 mg IV, repeated at 15-minute intervals
   D. 1,000 mg IV, repeated at 15-minute intervals
   E. 10 mg/min IV drip

Epinephrine

149. Present evidence indicates that the dose of epinephrine injected into the tracheobronchial tree should be
   A. 0.5 mg of a 1 : 10,000 solution (5.0 mL)
   B. 0.5 mg of a 1 : 1,000 solution (0.5 mL)
   C. 1.0 mg of a 1 : 1,000 solution (1.0 mL)
   D. 1.0 mg of a 1 : 10,000 solution (10.0 mL)
   E. 2.0 mg of a 1 : 1,000 solution (2.0 mL)

150. What is the effect of giving an IV bolus of epinephrine?
   A. Increase in arterial blood pressure
   B. Increase in systemic vascular resistance
   C. Increase in heart rate
   D. Bronchodilation
   E. All of the above

151. The actions of epinephrine include
   1. Increase in heart rate
   2. Depression of myocardial contractions
   3. Increase in systemic vascular resistance
   4. Decrease in myocardial oxygen consumption
   A. 1,2, and 4
   B. 2 and 3
   C. 1 and 2
   D. 4 only
   E. All of the above

152. Choose the false statement.
   A. Epinephrine may be given by the endotracheal route.
   B. Epinephrine may be used subcutaneously to treat allergic reactions.
   C. Epinephrine is normally given by the intracardiac route in cardiac arrest.
   D. Epinephrine should not be mixed with alkaline solutions.
   E. Epinephrine should be used cautiously in patients with angina or hypertension.

153. What is the recommended dosage of epinephrine (1 : 10,000 solution) for an adult patient in cardiac arrest?
   A. 5 mg initially, followed by 2.5 mg every 10 minutes as needed
   B. 5 mg initially, repeated every 5 minutes as needed
   C. 5 mL initially, repeated every 5 minutes as needed
   D. 0.5 mg initially, repeated every 10 minutes as needed
   E. 0.5 mg/kg initially, repeated every 10 minutes as needed

154. The indications for giving epinephrine include
1. ventricular fibrillation or a pulseless ventricular tachy-cardia
2. supraventricular tachycardia
3. asystole
4. asthma
5. bradycardia
    A. 1,2, and 3
    B. 1,3, and 4
    C. 2,4, and 5
    D. 3,4, and 5
    E. All of the above

Furosemide

155. Which statements are true of furosemide?
1. It may cause dehydration.
2. It may cause hypokalemia, with subsequent cardiac arrhythmias.
3. It may cause venous vasodilation.
4. Its effects begin about 60 minutes after administration
5. It may cause nausea and vomiting
    A. 1,2,3, and 5
    B. 2,3,4, and 5
    C. 1,2, and 3
    D. 2 and 3 only
    E. All of the above

156. For the treatment of pulmonary edema, what is the initial recommended dose of furosemide?
A. 40 mg
B. 80 mg
C. 2-4 mg/kg
D. 0.5-1 mg/kg
E. 10 mg/kg

157. Furosemide (Lasiz) may be contraindicated for
    A. a 78-year-old woman experiencing acute myocardial infarction with congestive heart failure
    B. a 60-year-old man with pulmonary edema
    C. a 40-year-old woman in hypertensive crisis
    D. a 37-year-old man with decreased urine output and gastrointestinal bleeding
    E. all of the above

Lidocaine

158. Which of the following is NOT a contraindication for administration of lidocaine?
    A. Sinus bradycardia
    B. Idioventricular rhythm
    C. Mobitz type I heart block
    D. Atrioventricular dissociation
    E. History of recent seizures

159. Which of the following is NOT an indication for use of lidocaine in suppression of premature ventricular contractions (PVCs)?
    A. Frequent PVCs (more than six each minute)
    B. PVCs that fall on the T wave (R or T phenomenon)
    C. Salvos of PVCs
    D. Multifocal PVCs
    E. Hypoxia

160. The dose for lidocaine should be decreased in patients
    1. with renal dysfunction
    2. with hepatic dysfunction
    3. with hypotension
    4. ages greater than 70
    5. taking calcium channel blockers
        A. 1,2, and 4
        B. 2 and 3
        C. 2,3, and 4
        D. 5 only
        E. All of the above

161. Lidocaine has which of the following characteristics?
    1. It is used to control ventricular arrhythmias.
    2. It is used to increase automaticity by slowing the rate of spontaneous phase 4 depolarization.
    3. It acts differently in acutely infarcted and normal myocardium.
    4. It has no significant effect on myocardial contractions, blood pressure, or atrioventricular conduction in doses used clinically.
    5. It is metabolized in the spleen and kidney.
        A. 1,2, and 4
        B. 1,3, and 5
        C. 3,4, and 5
        D. 1,3, and 4
        E. All of the above

162. An 82-year-old woman weighing 151 lb has multifocal PVCs. The initial dose of lidocaine should be
    A. 2 mg/min infusion
    B. 35 mg IV
    C. 50 mg IV
    D. 70 mg IV
    E. 2 mg/kg/min infusion

163. What symptoms are the best early signs of early lidocaine toxicity?
    A. Recurrent ventricular ectopy
    B. Seizures
    C. Slurred speech, altered level of consciousness
    D. Increased QRS interval
    E. Tachycardia

Miscellaneous Agents

164. What is NOT an indication for treatment with 50% dextrose solution (D_{50})?
   A. Hypoglycemia
   B. Coma of uncertain etiology
   C. Seizures of uncertain etiology
   D. Sweating and tachycardia in an insulin-dependent diabetic
   E. Hyperosmolality

165. Mannitol acts to
   A. block norepinephrine release
   B. block the vagus nerve
   C. produce a diuresis by increasing the osmolality of the blood
   D. reduce the carbon dioxide content of the blood
   E. change the functioning of the kidney's tubules

166. Aminophylline acts to
   A. dilate bronchioles by action on β-receptors
   B. increase breathing by a central effect
   C. decrease mucus production
   D. decrease mucosal edema
   E. relax smooth muscle in bronchioles

167. Which statement is true of digoxin?
   A. Its peak action occurs within 5 minutes of IV administration.
   B. It is useful for treating heart failure and tachyarrhythmias.
   C. It is helpful in the treatment of bradycardia.
   D. If the patient has atrial fibrillation with rapid ventricular response, it should not be used.
   E. It has a wide therapeutic "window."

168. Activated charcoal is useful in which ingestion?
   A. Methanol
   B. Cyanide
   C. Iron
   D. Organophasphate insecticides
   E. Aspirin

169. Which statement is NOT true about aminophylline?
    A. It is contraindicated in the presence of cardiac dysrhythmias.
    B. It may cause nausea and vomiting.
    C. It may cause seizures.
    D. It may be used in selected cases of pulmonary edema.
    E. It may be used to treat hypotension.

170. Contraindications for use of diphenhydramine (Benadryl) include all EXCEPT
    A. asthma
    B. severe allergic reaction
    C. glaucoma
    D. enlargement of the prostate
    E. ulcer disease with outflow obstruction

171. Side effects of diazoxide (Hyperstat) include all EXCEPT
    A. hypotension
    B. sodium retention
    C. water retention
    D. hyperglycemia
    E. bradycardia

172. Indications of hydrocortisone and other steroids include all EXCEPT
    A. treatment of severe allergic states
    B. treatment of toxic gas inhalation
    C. treatment of cerebral edema
    D. treatment of pulmonary edema
    E. treatment of asthma

173. Contraindications for hydrocortisone include
    A. severe allergic reactions
    B. hypotension
    C. cardiovascular collapse
    D. septic shock
    E. None of the above

174. Precautions to be followed in administration of magnesium sulfate include all EXCEPT
   A. do not use in pregnancy
   B. do not use in renal disease
   C. give intravenously only
   D. test deep tendon reflexes frequently
   E. do not use in heart block

175. Commonly used digitalis preparations include all EXCEPT
   A. digoxin
   B. digitoxin
   C. digitalis leaf, USP
   D. lanoxin
   E. gitaligin

176. Symptoms of digitalis toxicity include all EXCEPT
   A. blurred vision
   B. yellow-green tint to vision
   C. vomiting
   D. decreased respiration
   E. dysrhythmias

177. Oxytocin is used for
   A. control of toxemia of pregnancy
   B. control of bleeding of pregnancy between twin deliveries
   C. control of postpartum bleeding
   D. control of postvaginal surgical bleeding
   E. control of menopausal bleeding

178. Administration of calcium is appropriate in all of the following situations EXCEPT
   A. sodium fluoride poisoning
   B. hypocalcemia
   C. electromechanical dissociation
   D. verapamil overdose
   E. administration of large quantities of banked blood

179. Aminophylline side effects include all of the following EXCEPT
    A. bronchoconstriction
    B. ventricular irritability
    C. restlessness
    D. vomiting
    E. nausea

QUESTION 180: List the appropriate words or phrases.

---

180. Procainamide may be administered until any one of four situations has occurred. What are these situations?
    1. _____
    2. _____
    3. _____
    4. _____

QUESTIONS 181-229: Select the ONE most appropriate answer.

Narcotics

181. Which is NOT an effect of morphine sulfate?
    A. Reduction of myocardial oxygen consumption
    B. Peripheral venous constriction
    C. Analgesia
    D. Reduction of venous return to the heart
    E. Bradypnea

182. For the relief of chest pain, the proper dose of morphine sulfate is
    A. 5-10 mL every 10 minutes PRN IV
    B. 2-5 mg IV every 5 minutes until pain is relieved
    C. 0.5 mg IV every 5 minutes until pain is relieved
    D. 1 mg/kg IV initially, followed by one-half of this dose every 5 minutes PRN
    E. 10 mg IM

183. Normally, morphine sulfate is NOT administered to a patient with chest pain and
   A. tachypnea
   B. hypotension
   C. pulse 160
   D. recent surgery or anesthesia
   E. subendocardial myocardial infarction

184. Morphine is useful for a patient who is having an acute myocardial infarction because
   1. it helps to relax the patient
   2. it relieves the pain
   3. it causes vasodilatation and thus helps decrease the workload of the heart
   4. it stimulates the heart to pump better
      A. 1,2, and 3
      B. 1 and 3
      C. 2 and 4
      D. 4 only
      E. All of the above

185. In the field, an intramuscular injection of morphine sulfate may be used for
   A. relief of pain of 65% second- and third-degree burns
   B. myocardial infarction
   C. a crush injury of the hand in farm machinery
   D. a motor vehicle accident with chest trauma
   E. severe congestive heart failure

186. A side effect of intravenous administration of diazepam is
   A. hypoglycemia
   B. vomiting
   C. respiratory depression
   D. bradycardia
   E. postural hypertension

187. Indications for use of diazepam include all EXCEPT
- **A.** status epilepticus
- **B.** severe anxiety
- **C.** sedative prior to reduction of dislocations
- **D.** sedative prior to cardioversion
- **E.** treatment of respiratory depression

188. Contraindications for use of diazepam include all EXCEPT
- **A.** pregnancy
- **B.** alcohol or sedative drug use
- **C.** respiratory depression
- **D.** recent seizures
- **E.** hypotension

189. Indications for administration of naloxone include overdose with all EXCEPT
- **A.** meperidine
- **B.** propoxyphene
- **C.** nembutol
- **D.** morphine
- **E.** heroin

190. Side effects of administration of naloxone include all EXCEPT
- **A.** continued narcotic effects
- **B.** vomiting
- **C.** acute withdrawal reaction
- **D.** ventricular dysrhythmias
- **E.** respiratory depression

191. Contraindications to the use of nitrous oxide in the field include all EXCEPT
- **A.** altered state of consciousness
- **B.** pneumothorax
- **C.** abdominal distention
- **D.** shock
- **E.** myocardial infarction

192. The proper dose of nitrous oxide is
  A. determined at the scene by the paramedic
  B. 2 L/min flow
  C. 10 L/min flow
  D. determined by the patient
  E. 25% oxygen, 75% nitrous oxide

Vasoconstrictive Drugs

193. Which statements are true for dobutamine?
  1. It often produces reflex peripheral vasodilation.
  2. It directly increases renal perfusion.
  3. It often increases myocardial blood flow.
  4. It produces tachycardia less frequently than does dopamine.
  A. 1 and 4
  B. 3 and 4
  C. 1,3, and 4
  D. 1,2, and 4
  E. All of the above

194. Which is not an adverse effect of dobutamine?
  A. Increased myocardial oxygen consumption
  B. Tachydysrhythmias
  C. Increased systemic vascular resistance
  D. Deepened renal ischemia
  E. Headache

195. A dopamine infusion of 4 μg/kg/min has been started on a 72-year-old patient in circulatory shock with
  A. prolonged vomiting or diarrhea
  B. vomiting of bright red blood
  C. acute anterior myocardial infarction
  D. blunt abdominal injury
  E. 65% total body surface area second-degree burns

196. What should occur after administration of dopamine at a dose of $2-5$ μg/kg/min?
1. Renal perfusion increases.
2. Cardiac output increases.
3. Cerebral perfusion increases.
4. Myocardial contractility increases.
5. Mesenteric perfusion increases.
    A. 1,2, and 5
    B. 2 and 5
    C. 1,2, and 4
    D. 2 and 4
    E. 2,3, and 5

197. What is NOT a significant contraindication for administration of dopamine?
    A. Pheochromocytoma
    B. Tachyarrhythmias
    C. Ventricular fibrillation
    D. Hypovolemia
    E. Hepatic failure

198. Why is dopamine one of the drugs of choice for the treatment for cardiogenic shock?
1. It increases stroke volume and contractility of myocardial tissue.
2. It dilates peripheral vessels, thereby decreasing the workload of the heart.
3. It dilates myocardial vessels, possibly allowing more oxygen to reach myocardial tissue.
4. It does not appear to decrease renal blood flow in small doses.
    A. 1,2, and 4
    B. 1,3, and 4
    C. 2 and 4
    D. 1 and 3
    E. All of the above

199. Which is not an adverse effect of dopamine?
  A. Bronchospasm
  B. Decrease in blood pressure at low doses
  C. Tachyarrhythmias an/or ventricular ectopy
  D. Nausea and vomiting
  E. Headache

200. Which statement is NOT true of isoproterenol?
  A. It reduces the heart's oxygen consumption.
  B. It is indicted only for immediate, temporary control of significant bradycardia that is not responsive to atropine.
  C. It increases cardiac output.
  D. Once a pacemaker has been inserted, administration of isoproterenol should be discontinued.
  E. Isoproterenol can produce serious arrhythmias.

201. Which is NOT a common side effect of administration of isoproterenol?
  A. Palpitations
  B. Flushing
  C. Headache
  D. Dyspnea
  E. Lethargy

202. Isoproterenol has all of the following actions EXCEPT
  A. strengthened myocardial contractions
  B. increased cardiac output
  C. decreased peripheral resistance
  D. increased peripheral resistance
  E. increased heart rate

203. If isoproterenol (Isuprel) is administered too rapidly, what condition may result?
  A. Bronchospasm
  B. Status epilepticus
  C. Pulmonary edema
  D. Ventricular tachycardia
  E. Profound bradycardia

204. What action should follow a blood pressure drop after starting an isoproterenol (Isuprel) drip?
   A. Continue with treatment, since blood pressure will rise on its own.
   B. Stop the isoproterenol drip.
   C. Increase rate of drip to 6 μg/min.
   D. Increase rate of drip to 10 μg/min.
   E. Start dopamine at 2–5 μg/min.

205. What is NOT an adverse effect of norepinephrine?
   A. Decreased perfusion of the renal and mesenteric arteries
   B. Hypotension due to decreased cardiac output
   C. Atrioventricular dissociation
   D. Extension of infarct size
   E. Nausea and vomiting

206. What is the concentration of norepinephrine if 4 mg is added to 500 cc of D_5W?
   A. 8 mg/mL
   B. 16 mg/mL
   C. 16 μg/mL
   D. 8 μg/mL
   E. 0.8 μg/mL

207. In which clinical situation is the use of isoproterenol indicated?
   A. Asystole
   B. Bradycardia unresponsive to atropine
   C. Electromechanical dissociation
   D. Ventricular fibrillation
   E. Ventricular tachycardia

Vasodilator Drugs

208. When you administer nitroglycerin sublingually, what side effect would you WANT to occur?
   A. Nausea
   B. Hypotension
   C. Weakness
   D. Headache
   E. Hypertension

209. All of the following are acceptable indications for administration of intravenous nitroglycerine EXCEPT
   A. relief of pain of myocardial infarction
   B. relief of pain of unstable angina
   C. treatment of congestive heart failure
   D. treatment of pulmonary edema
   E. treatment of ventricular dysrhythmias

210. What is the initial dose of intravenous nitroglycerin?
   A. 5 μg/min
   B. 10 μg/min
   C. 20 μg/min
   D. 50 μg/min
   E. 0.5 μg/min

211. Why is nitroglycerin useful for treatment of angina?
   1. It increases the total peripheral resistance, thus lowering blood pressure.
   2. It may dilate blood vessels, thus increasing blood supply to heart tissue.
   3. It increases cardiac output.
   4. It may decrease the workload of the heart.
      A. 1,2, and 3
      B. 1 and 3
      C. 2 and 4
      D. 4 only
      E. All of the above

212. What is the main toxic effect of nitroglycerin?
    A. Hypertension
    B. Extension of the infarction site
    C. Hypotension
    D. Ventricular ectopy
    E. Nausea and vomiting

213. Which statement is NOT true of sodium nitroprusside?
    A. It is used in the emergency treatment of hypertension.
    B. It increases cardiac output.
    C. It decreases peripheral arterial resistance.
    D. It decreases peripheral venous resistance.
    E. It has a direct ionotropic effect on the heart.

214. What is the recommended starting dose of sodium nitroprusside?
    A. 0.5 μg/min
    B. 1–3 μg/min
    C. 4–6 μg/min
    D. 10–20 μg/min
    E. 50–100 μg/min

215. If 50 mg of sodium nitroprusside is added to 500 mL of D$_5$W, to administer a dose of 10 μg/min, what is the drip rate using a standard microdrop chamber?
    A. 6 drops/min
    B. 12 drops/min
    C. 18 drops/min
    D. 24 drops/min
    E. 48 drops/min

216. What is NOT a contraindication for use of nitroglycerin?
    A. Hypotension
    B. Hypovolemia
    C. Glaucoma
    D. Increased intracranial pressure
    E. Seizures

217. How often should you administer sublingual nitroglycerin for the relief of cardiac or anginal pain?
A. Every 2 minutes to a maximum of four doses
B. Every 5 minutes to a maximum of three doses
C. Every 10 minutes to a maximum of three doses
D. Every 15 minutes to a maximum of three doses
E. Every 20 minutes to a maximum of five doses

Verapamil

218. How does verapamil affect the cardiovascular system?
1. It causes systemic vasodilation.
2. It decreases systemic vascular resistance.
3. It increases myocardial oxygen consumption.
4. It decreases systolic blood pressure.
A. 1,2, and 3
B. 1,2, and 4
C. 2,3, and 4
D. All of the above

219. Verapamil is most useful in the treatment of
A. profound bradycardia
B. calcium overdose
C. propranolol toxicity
D. supraventricular tachydysrhythmias
E. cerebral failure

220. Which statements are true of verapamil?
1. It is effective for treating Prinzmetal variant angina.
2. Administration usually does not cause reduction in cardiac output.
3. In patients with left ventricular dysfunction, it may cause congestive heart failure.
4. It is a negative inotropic agent.
A. 1,3, and 4
B. 2,3, and 4
C. 1 and 4
D. 2 and 4
E. All of the above

221. The best immediate treatment for verapamil-induced hypotension is
    A. dopamine
    B. isoproterenol
    C. elevation of the lower extremities
    D. norepinephrine
    E. infusion of calcium

222. Contraindications to the use of verapamil include all EXCEPT
    A. cardiogenic shock
    B. concurrent use of propranolol
    C. atrioventricular block
    D. asthma
    E. hypotension

223. Significant side effects of verapamil include all EXCEPT
    A. hypotension
    B. ventricular tachycardia
    C. asystole
    D. cardiac arrest
    E. bradycardia

Therapy

224. For hemodynamically stable patients with ventricular tachycardia, the treatment of choice would be a trial of pharmocologic agents. The drug of choice is
    A. verapamil
    B. bretylium
    C. atropine
    D. lidocaine
    E. amrinone

225. Which of the following drugs does NOT have antiarrhythmic properties?
   A. Lidocaine
   B. Propranolol
   C. Heparin
   D. Procainamide
   E. Bretylium

226. The drug of choice for ventricular bigeminy is
   A. atropine
   B. lidocaine
   C. epinephrine
   D. isoproterenol
   E. bretylium

227. A 65-year-old patient is found to have crushing substernal chest pain and is vomiting. Her pulse is 30 and her blood pressure is 60 by palpation. An appropriate drug would be
   A. metarminol (Aramine)
   B. propranolol
   C. atropine
   D. neosynephrine
   E. morphine

228. You are called to an office building, where you find a 42-year-old man with severe chest pain that radiates to one shoulder, arm, and hand. He is short of breath, apprehensive, and restless, but his vital signs are normal. Your treatment should include
   A. aminophylline
   B. nitroglycerin
   C. vasopressors
   D. verapamil
   E. dobutamine

229. Which drug is associated with hallucinations, confusion, worsening of glaucoma, and blurred vision as side effects?
    A. Lidocaine
    B. Inderal
    C. Isuprel
    D. Atropine
    E. Epinephrine

QUESTION 230: Select the correct answers from the list of lettered items

---

230. Which drugs can be safely administered via endotracheal tube?
    A. Epinephrine
    B. Bretylium
    C. Atropine
    D. Lidocaine
    E. Valium
    F. Narcan
    G. Bicarbonate
    H. Inderal
    I. Verapamil
    J. Calcium chloride
    K. Sodium hydroxide

Explanatory Answers

105. C. A vial has a stopper. An ampule has the glass sealed over the top. (Ref. Caroline, p. 107)

106. A. In solutions, the chemical is completely dissolved in a liquid. Tinctures are solutions of the drug that are made with alcohol. Syrups, milks, and suspensions are immiscible drugs suspended in a liquid. Syrups have sugar and water to improve the taste. Lotions are suspensions designed for external use only. (Ref. Caroline, p. 106)

107. C. Note that the question is slowest to fastest. The oral (PO) route with onset of action in about 30 minutes is clearly the slowest, with subcutaneous (SQ) a close contender. Endotracheal (ET) and intravenous (IV) routes are both quite rapid, with onset of about one or two circulation times (about 60 to 90 seconds). (Ref. Caroline, pp. 106–108)

108. E. Epinephrine may be given by intravenous, subcutaneous, or endotracheal route. For mild asthmatic, the subcutaneous route will most likely be chosen. (Ref. Caroline, p. 108; Abbott, p. 214)

109. A. The chemical name is assigned shortly after discovery, describes the drug completely and exactly to chemists, and is often complex and easily forgotten. The trade and brand names are the same and are usually easily remembered mnemonics of the drug's pharmaceutical actions. Brand names are assigned by the company that markets the drug. The official name for a drug is usually the same as the generic name and is often a compromise between the chemical name and the trade name for ease of memory and description of action. The official name often has a designator after it to show where the strengths and properties of the drug are listed, such as USP (United States Pharmacopia) or NF (National Formulary). Generic names often indicate better what class of agent the drug belongs to than the brand name does. Amoxil is a specific brand name of amoxacillin, a penicillin derivative. (Ref. Caroline, p. 104)

110. C. Drugs that can be administered by the endotracheal route include Narcan, atropine, Valium, epinephrine (adrenalin), and lidocaine (the NAVEL drugs). The endotracheal route is the fastest of the listed routes of parenteral administration. An equally useful alternative might be the intraossesous route. (Ref. ACLS, p. 97; Abbott, p. 214)

111. D. Shock states, including cardiac arrest, are low-flow states for muscle. Because of this, absorption is slow and erratic from intramuscular injections. (Ref. Caroline, p. 107; Abbott, pp. 178–179)

112. B. The mnemonic NAVEL (Narcan, atropine, Valium, epinephrine, and lidocaine) describes those drugs that may be given by endotracheal administration. Specifically prohibited is bicarbonate, which tends to damage the lungs. (Ref. ACLS, pp. 99, 100; Caroline, p. 108)

113. C. The administered dose is 0.5 g/cc $\times$ 50 cc = 25 g (Ref. Grant, p. 579)

114. B. 5 g dextrose 5%/1,000 cc = 50 mg/cc; 50 mg/cc $\times$ 500 cc = 25,000 mg, or 25 g dextrose. (Ref. Caroline, pp. 122–128)

115. C. As above, 10% means 10 g in 1,000 mL of fluid, or 100 mg/mL. You need 5 mL of this solution to give 500 mg. (Ref. Caroline, pp. 122–128)

116. C. 185 lb = 86 kg; 0.01 mg/kg = .86 mg atropine; 1 cc = 1.0 mg; therefore, 0.86 mg atropine is to be administered. (Ref. Caroline, pp. 122–128)

117. B. 140 lb = 64 kg; 0.7 $\times$ 64 = 44.8 mg; 2 mL = 20 mg; therefore the patient would receive 4.48 mL, or, rounding off, 4.5 mL. (Ref. Caroline, pp. 122–128)

118. D. 2 g in 500 mL is the same as 4 g in 1,000 mL, or 4 mg/mL. (Ref. Caroline, pp. 122–128)

119. B. 1 mg in 500 cc is equivalent to 2 mg in 1,000 cc, or 2 μg/cc. (Ref. Caroline, pp. 122–128)

120. B. 1 : 10,000 = 1 g in 10,000 cc. This is equivalent to 1 mg in 10 cc. (divide both sides by 1,000), or 0.1 mg/cc (now divide both sides by 10). (Ref. Caroline, pp. 122–128)

121. B. 25 × 30 mg = 750 mg; 750/1,000 = .75 g. (Ref. Caroline, pp. 122–126)

122. Answers: (1) 0.45 g; (2) 24 mL; (3) 6,700 mg H_2O; (4) 143 lb. (1) 450 mg × 1,000 mg/g = 0.45 g. (2) 24 cc = 24 mL = 24 g (for all practical purposes). (3) 6.7 cc water weighs 6.7 g, 6.7 × 1,000 = 6,700 mg water. (4) 65 kg × 2.2 lb/kg = 143 lb. (Ref. Caroline, p. 121)

123. (1) 2.3 kg × 1,000 g/kg = 2,300 g (2) 0.03 kg × 1,000 g/kg × 1,000 mg/g = 30,000 mg. (3) 15 g × 60 mg = 900 mg. (4) 84 kg × 2.2 lb = 185 lb. (Ref. Caroline, p. 121)

124. (1) 1,000 mg/g, so 0.75 g = 750 mg. (2) 65 mL × 1/1,000 = 0.065 L. (3) 0.25 g × 60 mg/g = 15 mg. (4) 18 lb/2.2 lb/kg = 8 kg. (Ref. Caroline, p. 121)

125. 25 mL. 110/2.2 = 50 kg. 50 kg × 5 mg/kg = 250 mg; with concentration of 500 mg/50 cc, you need to give one-half the amount, or 25 cc. (Ref. Caroline, p. 121)

126. 80 mEq. 176/2.2 = 80 kg. Since the dose is 1 mEq/kg, you will give 80 mEq (or 80 cc). (Ref. Caroline, p. 126)

127. 45. 75 kg × 8 μg/kg/min = 600 μg/min; 200 mg/250 mL = 0.8 mg/mL; 0.6 mg/0.8 mg = 0.75; 60 × 0.75 = 45 drops/min. (Ref. Caroline, pp. 122–128)

128. 30. 2,000 μg/250 mL = 8 μg/mL; 4/8 × 6- = 30 drops/min. (Ref. Caroline, pp. 120–128)

129. 24. 64 kg × 5 μg/kg/min = 320 μg/min; 400 mg/500 mL = 0.8 mg/mL (800 μg/mL); 320/800 × 60 = 24 drops/min. (Ref. Caroline, pp. 120–128)

130. 45. 2,000 mg/500 mL = 4 mg/mL; (3 mg/min)/(4 mg/mL) × 60 drops/mL = 45 drops/min. (Ref. Caroline, pp. 120–128)

131. 75. 4,500 μg/500 mL = 8 μg/mL; (10 μg/min)/(8 μg/mL) × 60 drops/mL = 75 drops/min. (Ref. Caroline, pp. 120–128)

132. 20. 200 mg/250 mL = 0.8 mg/mL; 53 kg × 5μg/kg/min = 265 μg/min; (265 μg/min)/(800 μg/mL) × 60 drops/mL = 20 drops/min. (Ref. Caroline, pp. 120–128)

133. A. The maximum atropinizing dose for cardiac purposes is 2.0 mg. For patients with anticholinesterase inhibitor poisoning, far greater quantities may be needed. (Ref. Abbott, p. 202; ACLS, pp. 99–100)

134. B. Atropine will enhance atrioventricular conduction, increase the rate of sinus node discharge, and accelerate heart rate. It is therefore useful in treatment of symptomatic bradycardia. It is contraindicated when either urinary retention or increased intraocular pressure (glaucoma) is present, because it can worsen these conditions. In surgery, atropine is often used to decrease oral secretions. (Ref. Caroline, p. 133)

135. B. Propranolol, one of the first β-blocking agents, tends to slow heart rate and calm sympathetic discharge. These drugs have been found to be useful in the treatment of myocardial infarction, because they smooth out the effects of the sympathetic system during the crisis. Because the heart is then less stressed and subject to fewer dysrhythmias, the patient has a higher chance of survival. (*Note*: although the answer to this question is obvious when the pharmacology questions are sorted by category, the question appears in much the same form in at least six different state and regional paramedic examinations.) (Ref. Caroline, p. 155)

136. E. Since a primary effect of propranolol is to decrease sympathetic discharge, it also will block or blunt the effects of epinephrine at inappropriate times. This includes epinephrine release as a mechanism of compensation for hypoglycemia, hypovolemic shock, and congestive heart failure. Propanolol therefore worsens or masks these conditions. It will also cause bronchospasm, worsening asthma. (Ref. Caroline, p. 155)

137. A. β-Adrenergic blocking agents do not generally affect the renal or mesenteric blood flow. (Ref. ACLS, p. 123)

138. D. Congestive heart failure, nausea, hypotension, and bradycardia are well-documented effects of propranolol use. Asthmatics may experience worsening of their asthma. Lethargy or coma is not noted with propranolol. (Ref. ACLS, p. 124)

139. A. If congestive heart failure develops from an overdose of propranolol, the patient should be digitalized. (Ref. ACLS, p. 123)

140. C. Sodium bicarbonate is an alkalotic agent that is useful in treating metabolic acidosis. It has no direct nervous system effects. Since metabolic acidosis does not develop instantly, many short cardiac arrest treatment sequences will require no sodium bicarbonate therapy. (Ref. ACLS, p. 108)

141. A. Since sodium bicarbonate has nothing to do with the airway, it does not aid or hinder the ability to ventilate the patient. All other answers are correct. (Ref. ACLS, p. 108)

142. C. The recommended loading dose for all ages is 1 mEq/kg, followed every 10 minutes by about one-half the loading dose (0.5 mEq/kg). (Ref. ACLS, p. 108)

143. C. Needless to say, the use of sodium bicarbonate to treat hypernatremia is not appropriate. (Ref. ACLS, p. 109)

144. D. Both bretylium and lidocaine are administered at the same rates and concentrations when given as infusions for continuous control of arrhythmias. (Ref. ACLS, p. 105; Abbott, pp. 204–205, 225–226)

145. C. The most commonly found adverse reactions to bretylium are nausea and vomiting and hypotension. Fortunately, the hypotension is postural and is not usually a problem with patients in cardiac arrest or experiencing severe dysrhythmias. Precipitation of seizures is a problem with lidocaine, not with bretylium. (Ref. ACLS, p. 104; Abbott, p. 204)

146. B. Bretylium is a quaternary ammonium compound that both acts on the myocardium and has a direct adrenergic effect. The adrenergic effects are biphasic, with about 20 minutes of sympathomimetic effects followed by sympathetic blockade. During sympathetic blockade, the blood pressure and heart rate decrease. The antiarrhythmic effects of bretylium are not well understood but include prolongation of the action potential duration in normal but not infarcted tissue and improvement in the amplitude and upslope in the action potential. (Ref. ACLS, p. 104)

147. B. The initial dose of bretylium in the patient with refractory ventricular fibrillation is 5 mg/kg given rapidly intravenously. Only for a 70-kg patient is this dose exactly 350 mg. If the patient is being treated for recurrent or refractory ventricular tachycardia, the dose should be diluted in to 50 mL and given over 8–10 minutes. (Ref. ACLS, p. 105; Abbott, p. 204)

148. A. If the ventricular fibrillation persists, the dose is increased to 10 mg/kg and can be repeated every 15 minutes to a maximum dose of 30 mg/kg. If recurrent or refractory ventricular tachycardia persists, then a second injection of diluted bretylium may be given in 1–2 hours and every 6–8 hours after that. An alternative course is a continuous infusion of 1–4 mg/min. (Ref. ACLS, p. 105)

149. D. It appears that the drug is absorbed better in the dilute form. The appropriate dose is 1.0 mg or 10 cc. (Ref. Caroline, pp. 140, 141; ACLS, p. 99)

150. E. Cannon's "fight-or-flight" pictures the actions of epinephrine: Increased heart rate, force of ventricular contractions, blood pressure, coronary and cerebral blood flow, and automaticity are all manifestations of epinephrine. These increase myocardial oxygen consumption and systemic vascular resistance. At the same time, the patient should have relief of bronchoconstriction and profound tachycardia. (Ref. Caroline, p. 140; ACLS, pp. 98–99)

151. C. Epinephrine increases the "tone" of the heart and other muscles in the body, which increases the force of contractions of the heart and the constriction of peripheral blood vessels. Epinephrine also increases automaticity and rate of the heartbeat. Unfortunately, these effects also increase myocardial oxygen consumption. (Ref. ACLS, p. 98; Caroline, p. 140)

152. C. Epinephrine is indeed inactivated by alkaline solutions and should not be mixed with bicarbonate or other alkalis. It is well absorbed through the tracheobronchial tree and is used intravenously for the treatment of anaphylaxis as well as cardiac arrest. The intracardiac route is relatively dangerous and should probably not be used if either the endotracheal or the intraosseous route is available. (Ref. ACLS, p. 99; Caroline, p. 140; Abbott, p. 214)

153. C. The initial dose of epinephrine for an adult should be approximately 0.5 mg (5 mL of the 1 : 10,000 solution). This dose should be repeated every 5 minutes during the resuscitation or until a viable rhythm has been achieved. (Ref. ACLS, p. 98; Abbott, pp. 214–215)

154. B. Both asystole and bradycardia should be treated with a pacemaker. Atropine or isoproterenol can be used as temporizing agents until the external pacemaker is ready or until the patient is transported to a facility where a temporary pacemaker can be inserted. Epinephrine should not be used for these indications. (Ref. ACLS, p. 98)

155. A. The effects of furosemide begin almost immediately after intravenous infusion. (Ref. ACLS, p. 124; Abbott, p. 216; Caroline, p. 142)

156. D. For the patient who has never had furosemide, the usual starting point is 0.5–1 mg/kg of furosemide intravenously. For patients on chronic therapy, the starting dose may be higher. (Ref. ACLS, p. 124; Abbott, p. 216)

157. D. Obviously, if the renal failure is due to hypovolemic shock, it is not appropriate to administer a diuretic that also causes vasodilation! (Ref. Caroline, p. 142; Abbott, pp. 216–217)

158. E. Recent seizures are not a contraindication to use of lidocaine in the emergency setting. They may be a manifestation of lidocaine overdose, however. (Ref. Caroline, p. 145)

159. E. Premature ventricular contractions (PVCs) due to hypoxia should always be treated by correcting the hypoxia. The other indications of suppression of PVCs are appropriate. (Ref. Caroline, p. 145)

160. C. Lidocaine is detoxified in the liver, and anything that decreases liver function or blood flow increases the apparent effects of lidocaine. A person older than 70 years of age might also have a decreased volume of distribution and experience increased serum concentrations of lidocaine from standard doses. Long-duration infusions of lidocaine in the presence of renal failure may cause the accumulation of toxic metabolites, but this should not present a problem during short-term therapy with lidocaine. (Ref. ACLS, p. 103; Abbott, pp. 225–226)

161. D. Lidocaine is not normally toxic to the heart in doses used clinically. It is metabolized in the liver (see above). It does act differently in infarcted tissues than in normal tissues, slowing conduction velocity more in the injured tissue. It is the first-line agent for treatment of ventricular dysrhythmias. (Ref. ACLS, pp. 101–102; Abbott, pp. 225–226)

162. B. In patients over 70 years of age, the initial dose of 1 mg/kg should be reduced to 0.5 mg/kg. Such patients have a decreased volume of distribution and may have decreased hepatic clearance of the drug. (Ref. ACLS, p. 102; Abbott, pp. 225–226)

163. C. The first clinical indicators of lidocaine toxicity are usually associated with the central nervous system. Twitching, paresthesias, decreased hearing, and changes in the level of consciousness are frequently noted. A late effect is seizures. (Ref. ACLS, pp. 102–103; Abbott, pp. 225–226)

164. E. Since one of the side effects of administration of glucose is hyperosmolality, it is obvious that this is not an indication for use of D_{50}. (Ref. Caroline, p. 137)

165. C. Mannitol is an osmotic diuretic that only increases the osmolality of the serum with a subsequent "osmotic diuresis." The same effect could also be achieved by simply using glucose, and this is why patients in diabetic ketoacidosis are so dehydrated. (Ref. Caroline, p. 147; Abbott, p. 228)

166. E. Aminophylline's sole use in field medicine is as a bronchodilator. (Ref. Caroline, p. 133; Abbott, pp. 200–201)

167. B. Digitalis is most useful in treatment of the tachydysrhythmias (particularly atrial fibrillation with a fast ventricular response) and congestive heart failure. It has a peak action about 1–2 hours after administration and is useless in treatment of the bradydysrhythmias. (Ref. ACLS, p. 120)

168. E. Of the compounds listed, the only ingestion that is not a contraindication for use of activated charcoal is aspirin. (Ref. Caroline, p. 132)

169. E. Aminophylline is useful to achieve bronchodilation in cases of bronchospasm in asthma and chronic obstructive pulmonary disease. It should not be given in the presence of dysrhythmias and hypotension. Nausea and vomiting are frequently seen in cases of overdosage, with severe overdoses accompanied by seizures. (Ref. Caroline, p. 133)

170. B. Diphenhydramine is an antihistamine that is a useful adjunct in the treatment of anaphylaxis and severe allergic reactions. All of the others are valid contraindications to the use of diphenhydramine. (Ref. Caroline, p. 139)

171. E. Diazoxide is useful in the treatment of hypertensive crisis, although it has been supplanted by oral administration of nifedipine (a calcium channel blocking agent). It causes smooth muscle relaxation and thus vasodilation. Unfortunately, it also causes a reflex tachycardia. (Ref. Caroline, p. 138)

172. D. Steroids may have some place in the treatment of pulmonary edema due to toxic gas inhalation, but for congestive heart failure, they are not indicated. (Ref. Caroline, p. 143)

173. E. There are no contraindications to the use of a single dose of steroids in the field. In cases where large doses of steroids were administered too rapidly, hypotension and cardiovascular collapse have been reported (rarely). Although the use of steroids in cardiovascular collapse and shock is controversial, it is not contraindicated. (Ref. Caroline, p. 143)

174. A. Magnesium sulfate is indicated for the treatment of eclampsia (toxemia of pregnancy). All of the other answers are valid precautions for administration of magnesium. If knee-jerk reflexes become absent or depressed, then no more magnesium sulfate should be given. (Ref. Caroline, p. 146)

175. C. Digitalis leaf, USP, is a preparation of digitalis that is only rarely used because it is variable in effect from batch to batch. All of the other preparations are commonly used variants of digitalis. (Ref. Caroline, p. 159)

176. D. Decreased respiration is not seen in digitalis toxicity. All of the other answers are often seen, and the wise paramedic will learn to recognize them and ask the patient about them. (Ref. Caroline, p. 159)

177. C. Pitocin or oxytocin should be used only after the baby has been delivered. It will promote uterine contractions and thus decrease postpartum bleeding. (Ref. Caroline, p. 154)

178. C. Calcium was once considered a useful drug in the treatment of electromechanical dissociation. In fact, numerous studies have clearly indicated that it does not improve survival. Calcium is useful in calcium channel blocker overdose, hydroflouric acid burns, hypocalcemia resulting from hypoparathyroidism or administration of large quantities of banked blood. Fluoride poisoning causes rapid absorption of serum calcium and hence hypocalcemia. The chelating agents used to prevent clotting of banked blood likewise cause hypocalcemia. In addition, calcium may be useful in treatment of black widow spider bites and some other arthropod envenomations. (Ref. ACLS, p. 109; Caroline, p. 136)

179. A. Aminophylline is considered a bronchodilator. All of the other answers are side effects that should be considered by the paramedic. (Ref. Caroline, p. 133; Abbott, pp. 200–201)

180. Suppression of arrhythmia; hypotension; QRS widens by 50% of original width; administration of 1.0 g; It is important to know these endpoints for administration of procainamide. Procainamide may precipitate hypotension if administered too rapidly. It should be given in doses of 20 mg/min for a total maximum dose of 1 g. (Ref. ACLS, p. 103)

181. B. The vasodilation effect of morphine will increase the venous capacitance and reduce the preload on the heart. This reduction of myocardial work causes decreased myocardial oxygen consumption. Obviously, morphine also provides analgesia and sedation and slows respiration. (Ref. ACLS, p. 109; Abbott, pp. 229–230; Caroline, p. 148)

182. B. Morphine needs to be given until the pain is relieved. An appropriate dose to titrate this pain relief is 2–5 mg intravenously every 5 minutes. Another agent that should be considered for relief of pain in the patient with a myocardial infarction is nitroglycerin. Intramuscular injection should not be used in patients with suspected myocardial infarction. (Ref. ACLS, p. 109; Abbott, pp. 229–230)

183. B. Since morphine causes vasodilation, it would be unwise to administer it to a patient with hypotension. Perhaps if the patient has had an intravenous line and an antishock garment placed, it may be employed very cautiously. (Ref. ACLS, p. 109; Abbott, pp. 229–230)

184. A. Morphine relaxes the patient, relieves the patient's pain, and decreases the workload of the heart. It occasionally induces so much vasodilation that it causes postural hypotension, hardly helping the heart to pump better. (Ref. Caroline, p. 148; ACLS, p. 109)

185. C. Morphine may be safely used in the field as an intramuscular injection only for patients who are not in shock and do not have a significant potential for shock. Generally, this means that the patient should have an isolated limb injury with little chance of significant blood loss. In practical terms, because intramuscular injections take about 15 minutes to achieve full effect in the normal patient, other routes may provide better pain relief. The ONLY patient listed who has an isolated limb injury is in answer C. (Ref. Caroline, pp. 107; Abbott, pp. 229–230)

186. C. Diazepam is well known for its profound respiratory depression in selected patients. Whenever intravenous administration is contemplated, airway equipment should be close at hand. (Ref. Caroline, p. 138; Abbott, p. 210)

187. E. Diazepam should never be given to a patient with hypotension or respiratory depression. (Ref. Caroline, p. 138)

188. D. Diazepam is used to treat seizures, hence they are not a contraindication to its use. (Ref. Caroline, p. 139)

189. C. Naloxone can be useful in overdoses of narcotic agents. It is not usually effective in reversing coma from an overdose of barbiturates. (Ref. Caroline, p. 149)

190. E. Naloxone is the only narcotic antagonist available that does NOT cause respiratory depression. Naloxone often has a shorter duration of action than the narcotics that it reverses. This may cause the narcotic effects to surface when you least expect them. The solution to this problem is to give another dose of naloxone. (Ref. Caroline, p. 149)

191. E. An indication for the use of nitrous oxide is the pain of myocardial infarction. Abdominal distention or abdominal trauma where bowel sounds are not present is a contraindication, since absorption of nitrous oxide may worsen the distention. (Ref. Caroline, p. 151)

192. D. Nitrous oxide is self-administered by inhalation; thus the patient determines the dose. (Ref. Caroline, p. 151)

193. C. Dobutamine has no adverse effects on renal and mesenteric blood flow; it does not appear to increase it directly either. (Ref. ACLS, p. 118)

194. C. Dobutamine can exacerbate ischemia, including both myocardial and renal ischemia. A sympathomimetic, dobutamine can increase the potential for ventricular tachydysrhythmias. It does not cause a marked increase in systemic vascular resistance, however. (Ref. ACLS, p. 118)

195. C. All of the situations except C are manifestations of possible hypovolemia. Sympathomimetics (pressor agents) should not be used until an adequate fluid loading has been achieved in hypovolemia. (Ref. ACLS, p. 117; Abbott, pp. 211–212)

196. E. At this low dose of dopamine, cardiac output, myocardial contractility, and renal perfusion should all increase because of the "dopaminergic" effect on renal vessels and the direct effects on the myocardium. Mesenteric and cerebral blood flow will likewise increase with a low dose of dopamine. (Ref. ACLS, p. 117; Abbott, p. 211)

197. E. Dopamine is not broken down in the liver; hence liver failure such as cirrhosis is not a contraindication for administration of dopamine. (Ref. Caroline, p. 140)

198. B. Dopamine not only makes the heart beat more rapidly and forcefully, thus increasing cardiac output, it also seems to dilate myocardial vessels and may increase myocardial oxygenation. In small doses, it actually dilates the renal vessels. (Ref. Caroline, pp. 139–140; Abbott, p. 211)

199. A. Because dopamine is a sympathomimetic, one would expect a bronchodilatory effect, not bronchospasm. (Ref. ACLS, p. 117; Abbott, pp. 211–212)

200. A. Isoproterenol causes increased myocardial oxygen consumption, not decreased. (Ref. ACLS, p. 119)

201. E. Isoproterenol will cause tremulousness and palpitations, not lethargy. Other common side effects are listed. (Ref. Caroline, p. 144)

202. C. Isoproterenol decreases the peripheral resistance because it is a pure β-sympathetic agent. It also increases the automaticity of the heart, bronchodilates, and increases the rate and force of contractions of the heart. (Ref. ACLS, p. 119; Caroline, p. 144)

203. D. When any chronotropic agent is administered in too large a dose or too rapidly, the heart may respond with a rapid dysrhythmia, including ventricular tachycardia and ventricular fibrillation. (Ref. ACLS, p. 119; Abbott, pp. 220–221)

204. B. Whenever an adverse reaction is encountered after starting an infusion of medication, the medication should be discontinued and the situation reassessed. (Ref. ACLS, p. 119; Abbott, pp. 220–221)

205. C. Norepinephrine is a powerful vasoconstrictive agent that may cause hypoperfusion in renal and mesenteric vessels and may cause local necrosis if extravasated. The usual inotropic and chronotropic effects will cause an increase in myocardial oxygen consumption, sometimes to the detriment of ischemic tissues. Rarely, a drop in cardiac output will follow administration of norepinephrine, leading to hypotension. This is a reason to discontinue the drop. None of the sympathomimetic agents exacerbate a block, unless they cause an infarct to extend. (Ref. ACLS, p. 117)

206. D. 4 mg in 0.5 L is equivalent to 8 mg in 1 L or 8 μg/cc. (Ref. ACLS, p. 116)

207. B. Isoproterenol is considered a useful temporizing drug for bradycardia that does not respond to atropine. The most appropriate therapy for this condition is probably a pacemaker, and the isoproterenol may buy enough time to insert or apply the pacemaker. It should always be remembered that isoproterenol will increase myocardial rate and oxygen consumption at the expense of myocardial hypoxemia and potential increase in the infarct size. (Ref. ACLS, p. 119; Caroline, p. 144)

208. D. The side effect of headache is so common that you should suspect that your nitroglycerin has lost its potency if your patient does not complain. (Ref. Caroline, p. 150)

209. E. Nitroglycerin may dilate the coronary arteries sufficiently to relieve the pain of both myocardial infarction and atypical angina. The vasodilation effects will reduce the ventricular pre-load, often sufficiently to ease congestive heart failure and pulmonary edema. (Ref. ACLS, p. 122)

210. B. The usual starting dose of nitroglycerin is about 10 μg/min. This drug may then be titrated to appropriate effect. (Ref. ACLS, p. 123)

211. C. Nitroglycerin is a potent vasodilator. Because it dilates the blood vessels of the heart, it increases myocardial blood flow. At the same time, by decreasing the peripheral vascular resistance, it may decrease the workload of the heart. (Ref. Caroline, p. 150; Abbott, p. 233)

212. C. The major side effect of nitroglycerin is hypotension caused by the profound vasodilating effect. It can be treated with elevation of legs, MAST, fluids, and reduction or elimination of the nitroglycerin. The rapid effects of this drug allow easy titration to avoid this side effect. (Ref. ACLS, p. 123; Abbott, p. 233)

213. E. Nitroprusside, like nitroglycerin, has no direct effects on the heart; rather, it causes the heart to react to the induced peripheral vasodilation. This vasodilation will decrease peripheral resistance and thus increase cardiac output. (Ref. ACLS, p. 121)

214. A. Like nitroglycerin, sodium nitroprusside should be titrated to effect. A dose of about 0.5 μg/kg/min should be the initial starting point. (Calculation of dose by body weight is more accurate than an emperic dose.) (Ref. ACLS, p. 121)

215. A. If 50 mg is added to 0.5 L, then the concentration is 100 mg/L, or 100 μg/mL. Since each milliliter equals 60 drops, 6 drops will have 10 μg. (Ref. ACLS, p. 121)

216. E. Seizures are not a contraindication to the use of nitroprusside or nitroglycerin. You must be sure that the seizures are not a by-product of a process that also will increase intracranial pressure, however. (Ref. Caroline, p. 150)

217. B. Nitroglycerin may be given every 5 minutes to a maximum dose of three tablets in normal circumstances. Nitroglycerin is a short-lasting drug by both intravenous and sublingual routes. Only with long-acting oral preparations or skin patches will nitroglycerin have an appreciable effect beyond 10 minutes. (Ref. ACLS, p. 123; Abbott, p. 233)

218. B. The effect of decreasing systemic vascular constriction, systolic blood pressure, and cardiac rate would be to decrease, not increase, myocardial oxygen consumption. (Ref. ACLS, p. 106)

219. D. Calcium channel blockers, particularly the rapidly acting verapamil, are the agents of choice in treatment of the supraventricular tachydysrhythmias. (Ref. ACLS, p. 106)

220. E. Since verapamil both slows the heart and vasodilates the peripheral vessels, it will surely cause a decrease in cardiac output and may exacerbate cardiac failure. The other two statements are true. (Ref. ACLS, p. 106)

221. C. Since the hypotension induced by verapamil is postural, elevation of the feet should be the first step. If that does not work, the next step is infusion of calcium. (Ref. ACLS, p. 107)

222. D. Verapamil has little to do with the respiratory system and does not produce any bronchoconstriction. Asthma is not a contraindication to the use of verapamil. Hypotension that is not due to a rapid heart rate and decreased filling time of the ventricles would be expected to worsen with verapamil. Hypotension due to tachycardia might improve significantly, so verapamil may be used with caution in these patients. (Ref. Caroline, p. 158)

223. B. Verapamil will generally slow the heart rate, not increase it. It is used in selected patients to treat ventricular tachycardia associated with atrial flutter and atrial fibrillation. (Ref. Caroline, p. 158)

224. D. Lidocaine is considered by the ACLS working group of the American Heart Association to be the initial drug of choice for ventricular tachydysrhythmias. There is no overwhelming evidence that any other drug is superior to lidocaine in the treatment of these dysrhythmias. Lidocaine is faster working, less expensive, and better known than other drugs currently available. For these reasons, lidocaine should at least be the first drug considered in management of the ventricular dysrhythmia. (Ref. ACLS, p. 102)

225. C. Heparin is an anticoagulant, not an antiarrhythmic. (Ref. Caroline, pp. 135, 145, 155; ACLS, p. 103)

226. B. Although bretylium could conceivably be used for this indication, it is not considered the first-line drug of choice for treatment of dysrhythmias. Actually, the wise paramedic should check the patient's oxygenation before administering any other pharmacologic agents. (Ref. Grant, p. 93; Caroline, pp. 145, 298)

227. C. This patient appears to have had a myocardial infarction with a profound vagal response. An alternative explanation could invoke a third-degree block to explain the bradycardia. In either case, an appropriate response is 1 mg of atropine intravenously. (Ref. ACLS, p. 99; Caroline, pp. 119, 133, 134)

228. B. The only medication that you should immediately consider in this patient is nitroglycerin, which will physiologically relieve the pain of angina and myocardial infarction. (Ref. Caroline, p. 150)

229. D. The overdose of atropine can be characterized by a mnemonic: *Blind as a bat, mad as a hatter, red as a beet, dry as a bone, and hot as Hades.* These effects are caused by the decrease in sweating, tachycardia, and pupillary dilation effects of the atropine. Since the eye is widely dilated, the effects of glaucoma are worsened. (Ref. Caroline, p. 134)

230. A, C, D, E, F. Remember the mnemonic NAVEL (Narcan, atropine, Valium, epinephrine, lidocaine). (Ref. ACLS, pp. 99, 100; Caroline, p. 108)

6 Airway Management

General

231. Which condition can cause an upper airway obstruction?
  A. Epiglottitis
  B. Congestive heart failure
  C. Emphysema
  D. Asthma
  E. Pneumonia

232. The respiratory system has two functions. One is to make oxygen available for the body and the other is to
  A. remove excess oxygen from the body
  B. remove excess carbon dioxide from the body
  C. remove excess carbon monoxide from the body
  D. remove excess bicarbonate from the body
  E. remove excess nitrogen from the body

233. A leaflike structure that permits air to enter and closes to keep food and water from entering the trachea is the
  A. glottis
  B. epiglottis
  C. hard palate
  D. pleural sac
  E. alveolus

89

234. The final air space that represents the unit of gas exchange is the
   A. alveolus
   B. respiratory bronchiole
   C. capillary system
   D. pleural space
   E. glottis

235. The amount of air exchanged in a normal breath (tidal volume) is approximately
   A. 500 cc
   B. 150 cc
   C. 1,000 cc
   D. 3,700 cc
   E. 15,000 cc

236. The point where the trachea bifurcates into right and left mainstem bronchi is called the
   A. carina
   B. vallecula
   C. glottis
   D. uvula
   E. epiglottis

237. The total lung capacity of an adult is
   A. 500 cc
   B. 1,500 cc
   C. 3,000 cc
   D. 6,000 cc
   E. 15,000 cc

238. Ambient air contains
   A. 18% oxygen
   B. 21% oxygen
   C. 25% oxygen
   D. 35% oxygen
   E. 42% oxygen

239. Respiratory acidosis can be caused by
   A. hypoventilation
   B. chronic obstructive pulmonary disease (COPD)
   C. mechanical obstruction
   D. near drowning
   E. all of the above

240. Early pulmonary edema most likely will exhibit
   A. stridor
   B. a prolonged expiratory phase
   C. crackles
   D. absent breath sounds
   E. wheezes

241. The production of which acid increases when the supply of oxygen to the tissues is insufficient?
   A. Uric
   B. Citric
   C. Amnionic
   D. Hypoxic
   E. Lactic

242. A patient with a normal tidal volume has an arterial P_{CO_2} of 20. This individual's respiratory rate probably
   A. is slow (less than 12 breaths per minute)
   B. is normal (about 12 breaths per minute)
   C. is fast (greater than 20 breaths per minute)
   D. cannot be evaluated from the data given
   E. is none of the above

243. A 26-year-old woman is found unconscious behind the local minimarket. Her arms are covered with needle tracks and her pupils are fully constricted. Her respiratory rate is 6 per minute. Which body system is malfunctioning?
   A. CNS
   B. Air passages and lungs
   C. Muscles
   D. Tongue
   E. Endocrine system

244. The most probable values for this person's blood gases are
A. elevated O_2, low CO_2
B. high O_2, high CO_2
C. low O_2, high CO_2
D. low O_2, low CO_2

245. This patient's pH is probably
A. acidotic
B. normal
C. alkalotic

246. You are attending a 54-year-old man who is complaining of dyspnea. He is a two-pack-per-day smoker who acknowledges he has a smoker's cough. Over the last few days the cough has become more bothersome and the sputum is now yellow-green and streaked with blood. He appears flush, somewhat cyanotic, and in obvious respiratory distress. His vital signs are pulse 112, BP 150/90, respirations 38, and temperature 102. On auscultation of the chest, rhonchi and rales are heard on the right side. You suspect he has
A. toxic inhalation exposure
B. asthma
C. bacterial pneumonia
D. congestive heart failure
E. aspiration pneumonia

247. For the patient in Question 246, what is your course of action after you have ensured an adequate airway, placed him in an upright position, and administered oxygen?
A. Perform a needle aspiration of the left lung
B. Start IV, diuretics, and morphine (after checking with base)
C. Intubate the patient with an endotracheal tube
D. Administer 1.0 g of either a cephalosporin or ampicillin if the patient is not allergic to these antibiotics
E. Transport him to the hospital

248. After being awakened from her sleep because of coughing and shortness of breath, this 65-year-old woman has called for an ambulance. You find the woman apprehensive and breathing with difficulty. She tells you she is being treated for hypertension and takes digoxin and a diuretic. Her pulse is 122, BP is 192/112, and respirations are 36 per minute. Her temperature is normal. Diffuse rhonchi, wheezes, and rales are heard on auscultation of the chest. You note jugular venous distension when the bed is at a 45° angle. The most likely cause for this clinical picture is

    A. pneumothorax

    B. epiglottitis

    C. pneumonia

    D. asthma

    E. congestive heart failure

249. What is the most immediate cause of death in a near drowning victim?

    A. Electrolyte abnormalities

    B. Laryngospasm

    C. Pulmonary edema

    D. Hypoxia

    E. Hemolysis of red blood cells

250. Approximately how much inhaled air remains in the dead air space in the respiratory system?

    A. 100 mL

    B. 150 mL

    C. 200 mL

    D. 350 mL

    E. 450 mL

251. Oxygen is carried in the blood principally as

    A. a part of the carbon dioxide molecule

    B. dissolved in the plasma

    C. a chemical combination with albumin

    D. a chemical combination with hemoglobin

    E. a chemical combination with myoglobin

252. What is the normal flow rate when using a partial rebreathing mask?
   A. 2–4 L/min
   B. 4–6 L/min
   C. 6–10 L/min
   D. 8–12 L/min
   E. 12–14 L/min

253. What percentage of oxygen is delivered with a partial rebreathing mask if the flow rate is properly adjusted?
   A. 20–40%
   B. 35–60%
   C. 45–75%
   D. 70–90%
   E. 80–90%

254. If the flow rate is properly set, what percentage of oxygen is delivered with a simple face mask?
   A. 10–20
   B. 20–30
   C. 25–40
   D. 50–60
   E. 60–80

255. What is the flow rate usually used with a simple face mask?
   A. 2–4 L/min
   B. 4–6 L/min
   C. 8–12 L/min
   D. 10–15 L/min
   E. None of the above

256. What flow rate is normally used with a nasal cannula?
   A. 2–4 L/min
   B. 4–6 L/min
   C. 6–8 L/min
   D. 8–12 L/min
   E. None of the above

257. At the proper flow rate, what is the percentage of oxygen delivered with a nasal cannula?
    A. 20–30
    B. 25–40
    C. 35–45
    D. 45
    E. 60–80

258. Which is the most commonly found pathophysiology of emphysema?
    A. Decreased dyspnea
    B. Dilation of the bronchi
    C. Decreased elasticity of the lung
    D. Decreased size of the alveolar sacs
    E. Air between the lung and the parietal pleura

259. A 4-year-old child is discovered lying on the floor in his parents' bedroom with a plastic bag over his head. He appears cyanotic. Which condition does he have?
    A. Hypopion
    B. Hypoxemia
    C. Hyperkalemia
    D. Hyperemia
    E. Hypofunctioning hemoglobin

260. Fluid-filled, nonfunctional alveoli are characteristic of
    A. pleurisy
    B. pulmonary edema
    C. COPD
    D. carcinoma
    E. pulmonary emboli

261. Coughing often relieves this partial larger airway obstruction usually caused by mucus. The rattling noises heard in the throat or bronchi in this condition are called
    A. rhonchi
    B. wheezes
    C. stridor
    D. rales
    E. snoring

262. Fluid in the smaller airways produces moist, fine bubbling or crackling sounds called
    A. wheezes
    B. rhonchi
    C. rales
    D. stridor
    E. snoring

263. Initially, how many breaths should be administered to a patient in respiratory arrest?
    A. 1
    B. 2
    C. 3
    D. 4
    E. 6

264. What type of respiratory pattern does a patient have if respirations, which are rapid and irregular in rate and volume, alternate with periods of apnea?
    A. Hyperpnea
    B. Biot's breathing
    C. Kussmaul breathing
    D. Cheyne–Stokes breathing
    E. Hyperventilation

265. In a comatose patient, the most common cause of airway obstruction is
    A. asthma
    B. the tongue
    C. foreign bodies
    D. teeth (dentures)
    E. the epiglottis

266. An individual who is unable to create a normal negative intrapleural pressure because of injury may have
    A. asthma
    B. a flail chest
    C. a pulmonary embolus
    D. hemothorax
    E. pulmonary contusion

267. Which sign is most likely to be found with early pulmonary edema?
A. Wheezes
B. Absent breath sounds
C. Crackles
D. Stridor
E. Prolonged expiratory phase

268. What causes the signs and symptoms of "hyperventilation syndrome"?
A. Hypoxemia
B. Respiratory acidosis
C. Poor pulmonary perfusion
D. Hypocarbia
E. Hypoventilation

269. A sudden onset of chest pain and dyspnea in an elderly bedridden patient with a broken hip could be the result of
A. hyperventilation
B. hypoventilation
C. poor lung perfusion
D. asthma
E. none of the above

270. Contraction of the chest muscles to expand the rib cage and downward movement of the diaphragm initiate which phase of breathing?
A. Respiration
B. Inspiration
C. Ventilation
D. Expiration
E. Exhalation

271. With each exhalation, bright red, frothy blood bubbles from the patient's mouth. This is a sign of possible
A. respiratory arrest
B. lung damage
C. airway obstruction
D. abdominal obstruction
E. ruptured abdominal aortic aneurysm

272. The signs and symptoms of a tension pneumothorax include all of the following EXCEPT
    A. muffled heart sounds
    B. tracheal deviation
    C. cyanosis
    D. increasing dyspnea
    E. absence of breath sounds

273. With which condition would you see paradoxical chest movement?
    A. flail chest
    B. tension pneumothorax
    C. Cheyne–Stokes breathing
    D. mediastinal shift
    E. asthma

274. A patient with acute epiglottitis would be seriously threatened by
    A. receiving a high percentage of humidified oxygen
    B. being placed in the steam from a shower or bath
    C. auscultation of the chest with a cold stethoscope
    D. examination of the oropharynx with a tongue depressor
    E. an oxygen mask delivering O_2 at 8 L/min

275. During expiration, small airway narrowing can be heard as
    A. wheezes
    B. rales
    C. rhonchi
    D. B and C
    E. stridor

276. Diaphragmatic breathing is characterized by
    A. weak and rapid respirations with paradoxical chest movements
    B. weak and rapid respirations with little chest movement
    C. weak and rapid respirations with normal chest movement
    D. use of the abdominal muscles in exhalation
    E. strong and rapid respirations with movement of the abdomen

277. Cricothyrotomy is indicated under which circumstances?
    A. When lower airway obstruction is present.
    B. When long-term respiratory support will be needed.
    C. When facial or laryngeal trauma or edema is present.
    D. In lieu of intubation in infants and small children.
    E. When the patient has inhaled toxic gas.

278. Kussmaul's respirations
    A. are often noted in strokes and head trauma
    B. are grossly irregular with a waxing and waning pattern
    C. represent an attempt to reverse metabolic acidosis
    D. represent an attempt to blow off cyanide or carbon monoxide
    E. indicate impending pulmonary edema

QUESTION 279: For each numbered item, select the most closely related lettered item. (The same letter may be used more than once.)

---

279. Match the following descriptive phrases with the correct terms.
    1. _____ A harsh, high pitched sound heard on inspiration with upper airway obstruction
    2. _____ A whistling sound often associated with asthma
    3. _____ Fine, moist sounds associated with fluid in the smaller airways
    4. _____ A low-pitched sound produced by partial upper airway obstruction
    5. _____ Rattling noises in the throat or bronchi often caused by mucus

    A. rales
    B. wheezing
    C. rhonchi
    D. stridor
    E. snoring

Intubation

QUESTIONS 280–282: Fill in the appropriate words or phrases.

280. Endotracheal tube placement in the field is best verified by

    _____

281. Name two benefits of endotracheal intubation.
    1. _____
    2. _____

282. Name three complications of intubation.
    1. _____
    2. _____
    3. _____

QUESTIONS 283–311: Select the ONE most appropriate answer.

---

283. Which is not an indication for an endotracheal intubation?
    A. Vomiting comatose patient
    B. Barbiturate overdose with respirations of 6 per minute
    C. Inhalation injury with respiratory difficulties
    D. Cardiac arrest
    E. Unconscious patient with an intact gag reflex

284. What is the most important factor in determining the correct position of an endotracheal tube?
    A. Anterior and downward displacement of the tongue
    B. Visualization of the cords
    C. Correct head and neck position
    D. Removal of all dentures and foreign material
    E. Use of a straight laryngoscopy blade

285. You can use an esophageal obturator airway (EOA) on a patient who
   A. is under 16 years old
   B. has a gag reflex
   C. is breathing 4–8 times per minute
   D. has known esophageal disease
   E. is none of the above

286. What is the major complication in use of an EOA?
   A. Intubation of the trachea
   B. Esophageal tears
   C. Aspiration if removed before endotracheal intubation
   D. Gastric distension
   E. All of the above

287. What piece of equipment is not needed for an EOA insertion?
   A. Water-soluble lubricant
   B. EOA mask
   C. Laryngoscope and blades
   D. 30-mL syringe
   E. All of the above

288. When inserting an EOA tube, the head should be
   A. hyperextended
   B. hyperflexes
   C. in the neutral or slight flex position
   D. in any position

289. Once a patient with status asthmaticus has been intubated, what is the most common reason for ABRUPT worsening of the condition?
   A. Pneumothorax
   B. Atelectasis
   C. Cerebrovascular accident
   D. Aerophagia
   E. Dysbaric air embolism

Acid-Base Balance

290. What are the principal lines of defense for regulation of acid–base balance?
1. Buffer system
2. Respiratory system
3. Renal system
4. Endocrine system
    A. 1,3
    B. 1,2, and 3
    C. 2 and 4
    D. 1,2, and 4
    E. All of the above

291. The most rapid acting of these defense mechanisms is
    A. the endocrine system
    B. the buffer system
    C. the renal system
    D. the respiratory system
    E. A–D (they all act equally quickly)

292. The normal pH of the blood is
    A. 7.30–7.40
    B. 7.25–7.35
    C. 7.35–7.45
    D. 7.45–7.50
    E. 7.50–7.70

293. What is the most common acid–base abnormality found in a cardiac arrest victim?
    A. Respiratory alkalosis and metabolic acidosis
    B. Respiratory acidosis and metabolic acidosis
    C. Respiratory acidosis and metabolic alkalosis
    D. Respiratory alkalosis and metabolic alkalosis

294. Which blood gas values most accurately demonstrate a combined respiratory and metabolic acidosis?
    A. pH 7.75, Pco_2 14, Po_2 118
    B. pH 7.40, Pco_2 65, Po_2 50
    C. pH 7.15, Pco_2 65, Po_2 40
    E. pH 7.40, Pco_2 19, Po_2 90

295. The normal P_{CO} of arterial blood at sea level is
   A. 10–20
   B. 20–40
   C. 40–50
   D. 60–70
   E. 70–80

296. The normal P_O of arterial blood at sea level is about
   A. 10–30
   B. 30–60
   C. 70–100
   D. 95–105
   E. 140–150

297. How do the arterial values for pH, P_{CO_2}, and P_{O_2} in those individuals living at higher altitudes differ from those who live at sea level?
   A. pH is higher
   B. pH is lower
   C. P_{O_2} is lower and the P_{CO_2} is higher
   D. P_{O_2} and P_{CO_2} are lower

298. Which of the following situations will NOT cause hyperventilation?
   A. Acute stress reaction
   B. Diabetic ketoacidosis
   C. Cyanide intoxication
   D. Running three 7-minute miles
   E. Alcohol intoxication

299. A patient with blood gas values of pH 7.15, P_{CO_2} 60, P_{O_2} 66 is suffering from
   A. respiratory acidosis
   B. metabolic acidosis
   C. respiratory alkalosis
   D. metabolic alkalosis

300. Blood gas values of pH 7.30, Pco_2 34, Po_2 80 signify which condition?
   A. Respiratory acidosis
   B. Metabolic acidosis
   C. Respiratory alkalosis
   D. Metabolic alkalosis

301. Which condition is associated with blood gas values of pH 7.50, Pco_2 21, Po_2 110?
   A. Respiratory acidosis
   B. Metabolic acidosis
   C. Respiratory alkalosis
   D. Metabolic alkalosis

302. What etiology would cause blood gas values of pH 7.10, Pco_2 40, and Po_2 84 during a cardiac arrest?
   A. Aerobic metabolism
   B. Nasogastric suction
   C. $NaHCO_3$ therapy
   D. Anerobic metabolism
   E. Diabetic ketoacidosis

303. If blood gases cannot be determined, what is the initial dose of $NaHCO_3$ for a 112-lb female cardiac arrest victim?
   A. 25 mL
   B. 50 mL
   C. 75 mL
   D. 100 mL

304. If blood gases cannot be obtained, sodium bicarbonate should be given
   A. every 5 minutes
   B. every 10 minutes
   C. every 15 minutes
   D. every 30 minutes

305. Respiratory acidosis is usually associated with which important clinical condition?
   A. Chronic bronchitis, where gas exchange in the lungs is obstructed and the CO_2 cannot be properly eliminated
   B. During a cardiac arrest, when too much HCO_3 is given
   C. Hyperventilation with its decrease in P_{CO_2} (H_2CO_3)
   D. Ketoacidosis (as in a diabetic with an accumulation of organic acids) and lactic acidosis (such as follows the hypoperfusion during a cardiac arrest)

306. Which important clinical condition can lead to metabolic alkalosis?
   A. ketoacidosis or lactic acidosis
   B. hyperventilation
   C. administration of too much HCO_3 during a cardiac arrest
   D. chronic bronchitis

307. Carbon dioxide elimination is
   A. directly proportional to minute volume
   B. directly proportional to tidal volume
   C. directly proportional to respiratory rate
   D. decreased with administration of sodium bicarbonate
   E. decreased with administration of epinephrine

308. Which important clinical condition can lead to metabolic acidosis?
   A. Administration of too much HCO_3 during a cardiac arrest
   B. Chronic bronchitis
   C. Hyperventilation
   D. Overdose of heroin
   E. Ketoacidosis

309. Which important clinical condition can lead to respiratory alkalosis?
  A. Hyperventilation
  B. Ketoacidosis or lactic acidosis
  C. Administration of too much HCO_3 during a cardiac arrest
  D. Chronic bronchitis
  E. Tension pneumothorax

310. Which of the following abnormalities may be corrected by increased ventilation?
  A. metabolic acidosis
  B. respiratory acidosis
  C. metabolic alkalosis
  D. respiratory alkalosis

311. A blood gas reading shows a $Paco_2$ of 70 mm Hg. You can definitely say that this patient
  A. has an increased tidal volume
  B. has a metabolic acidosis
  C. has a metabolic alkalosis
  D. is hypoventilating
  E. has a chronic lung disease

Explanatory Answers

231. A. The other conditions are lower airway diseases. (Ref. Caroline, p. 196)

232. B. The major function of the lungs is to add oxygen and remove carbon dioxide from the body. (Ref. Grant, p. 135; Caroline, p. 171)

233. B. The valve that keeps food and water from the respiratory tract is the epiglottis. This closes during swallowing. (Ref. Caroline, p. 168)

234. A. The smallest of the gas exchange areas is the alveoli, the terminal lung area for the gas exchange. (Ref. Grant, p. 135; Caroline, p. 168)

235. A. A normal size breath is approximately 500 cc. (Ref. Grant, p. 137; Caroline, p. 171)

236. A. The bifurcation of the trachea is called the carina. At this point, the right mainstem bronchus continues somewhat down and to the right, the left has a sharper angle to the left. (Ref. Caroline, p. 171)

237. D. The total lung capacity is about 6 L in the adult. Of that, only a small portion is exchanged with each breath. (Ref. Caroline, p. 170)

238. B. Ambient or room air contains about 21% oxygen at all terrestrial altitudes. (Ref. Grant, p. 138; Caroline, p. 172)

239. E. Anything that causes a decrease in the ability of the alveolus to exchange carbon dioxide will cause respiratory acidosis. (Ref. Grant, p. 141; Caroline, p. 125)

240. C. Rales are the most common early finding of pulmonary edema from any cause. (Ref. Caroline, p. 181)

241. E. Unfortunately, hypoxic refers to the conditions under which lactic acid is formed. Anaerobic cellular metabolism will produce lactic acid. (Ref. Caroline, p. 172)

242. C. The low Pco_2 should clue you into the probable hyperventilation. Because the tidal volume is normal, the respiratory rate must have increased. (Ref. Caroline, p. 175)

243. A. See comment on Question 245. (Ref. Caroline, p. 183)

244. C. See comment on Question 245. (Ref. Caroline, p. 183)

245. A. This is the typical "toxidrome" of a narcotic CNS depressant. Failure to breathe means less O_2 and far more CO_2 in the bloodstream, leading to a classic respiratory acidosis. (Ref. Caroline, p. 183)

246. C. This is the classic picture of a bacterial pneumonia; consolidation of the lung, dyspnea, fever, and a productive cough. You might ask the patient if he has had any shaking chills (rigors). (Ref. Caroline, p. 208)

247. E. Nothing you can give this patient will help, and antibiotics are needed to cure the disease. Unfortunately, you are not certified to administer or prescribe antibiotics. A needle aspiration is not indicated, and it is unlikely that this patient will need emergency endotracheal intubation. (Ref. Caroline, p. 208)

248. E. This is obviously congestive heart failure. The jugular venous distension should alert you to volume overload, and the patient's medications are those of a patient with a cardiac disease. It is unlikely that the adult patient with asthma would not be taking a bronchodilator. All that wheezes is not asthma. (Ref. Caroline, pp. 199–200, 209, 269)

249. B. The most immediate cause of death is hypoxia. The hypoxia may be caused by pulmonary edema or by laryngospasm, or by aspiration of fluid and displacement of the oxygen. Electrolyte abnormalities are quite rare in drowning patients. (Nancy Caroline did not consult the most recent literature in her discussion on drowning. Electrolyte abnormalities occur only after 22 cc of fluid per kilogram body weight or more is aspirated. In the vast majority of drowning and near drowning patients, there is less than 10 cc of fluid aspirated per kilogram.) (Ref. Caroline, p. 209)

250. B. The dead space is the air within the trachea and larger bronchi that does not enter the alveoli. It is called "dead" space because there is no gas exchange, yet the lungs must do the work of moving this air. (Ref. Caroline, p. 121)

251. D. Hemoglobin carries the bulk of the oxygen in the bloodstream at normal atmospheric pressures. Myoglobin serves a similar purpose within muscle cells. Dissolved oxygen is important only when dealing with hyperbaric oxygenation. (Ref. Caroline, p. 72)

252. C. A partial rebreathing mask can provide an oxygen concentration of about 35% to 60% oxygen with flow rates between 6 and 10 L/min. (Ref. Caroline, p. 218)

253. B. See comment on Question 252. (Ref. Caroline, p. 218)

254. D. A simple face mask can deliver up to 60% oxygen when the flow rate is set between 8 and 12 L/min. (Ref. Caroline, p. 218)

255. C. In general, the flow rate should be set at 8–12 L/min. With lower flow rates, the amount of oxygen delivered will decrease as air is drawn in from around the mask. (Ref. Caroline, p. 218)

256. B. Although a nasal cannula are a very comfortable and unobtrusive way for the patient to receive supplemental oxygen, it provides only a modest augmentation of the patient's normal inspired oxygen content. If the flow rate is increased beyond about 6 L, the nasal passages will be dried and irritated. At a flow rate of about 6 L, the inspired oxygen concentration is about 35%. (Ref. Caroline, p. 218)

257. B. See comment on Question 256.

258. C. Emphysema is characterized by destruction of the alveolar walls, with subsequent distension of the alveoli. This loss of elasticity cause the alveoli to become nonfunctional, with an increase in the size of the alveolar sacs and increased dyspnea, first with exertion, then with rest. Chronic bronchitis is dilation and destruction of the bronchi. Air between the lung and the parietal pleura is called a pneumothorax. (Ref. Caroline, p. 198)

259. B. Hypoxemia is a low level of oxygen in the blood. Logically, interruption of the air supply by a plastic bag can lead to hypoxemia. By the way, a hypopion is a condition with purulent fluid in the anterior chamber of the eye. (Ref. Caroline, p. 176)

260. B. Of the diseases listed, the only one with fluid filled alveoli is pulmonary edema. Pulmonary emboli plug the circulation to the lungs, and pleurisy affects the lining of the lungs. Chronic obstructive pulmonary disease destroys the lung tissue, and carcinoma of the lung will replace the lung tissue with another "wild" tissue that does not function. (Ref. Caroline, p. 208)

261. A. Rales are fine moist "Rice Krispy"-like noises, while wheezes are whistling-like noises. Rhonchi are the rattling noises of the larger lower airways. Stridor and snoring are both upper airway noises. (Ref. Caroline, p. 208)

262. C. See comment on Question 261. (Ref. Caroline, p. 181)

263. B. This represents a change from the "stack 4 breaths" protocol in prior years. (Ref. Caroline, p. 316)

264. D. This is the classic description of Cheyne-Stokes breathing, with cycles of rapid breathing followed by a period of apnea and a gradual acceleration of breathing rate back to hyperpnea. (Ref. Caroline, p. 47)

265. B. The most common cause of airway obstruction in an unconscious patient remains the tongue as it flops backward against the pharynx. This is easily remedied by simply using the head tilt or the jaw thrust maneuver. (Ref. Caroline, p. 105; ACLS, p. 27)

266. B. Although massive hemothorax and an open pneumothorax (sucking chest wound) can both obstruct the normal intrathoracic pressure cycle, the most common cause is a flail segment that moves. (Ref. Caroline, p. 203; BTLS, pp. 36, 39)

267. C. Crackles, or rales, are most often found with early pulmonary edema. Wheezes are a less frequent but important finding in pulmonary edema, eg, "cardiac asthma." (Ref. Caroline, pp. 269, 181)

268. D. Numbness, tingling, and carpopedal spasm are hallmarks of hyperventilation's fall in arterial CO_2 concentration because of the rapid respiratory rate. (Ref. Caroline, p. 215)

269. C. A pulmonary embolus is more common in the bedridden patient and in those with recent trauma or surgery. Needless to say, poor lung perfusion is a hallmark of the pulmonary embolus. (Ref. Caroline, p. 212)

270. B. Inspiration occurs when the chest expands and the diaphragm contracts. The resultant negative intrathoracic pressure draws in air. (Ref. Caroline, p. 33)

271. B. Bright red froth would probably be caused by arterial blood. Of the conditions listed, only damage to the lung would produce bloody froth from the mouth. (Ref. Caroline, p. 169)

272. A. Muffled heart sounds are a sign of cardiac tamponade, not tension pneumothorax. (Ref. Caroline, pp. 204–205)

273. A. A flail segment is needed to develop paradoxical respirations. (Ref. Caroline, p. 207)

274. D. Irritation of the epiglottis may lead to respiratory obstruction. Use of a tongue depressor may provide this irritation and therefore is quite dangerous in the patient with suspected epiglottitis. (Ref. Caroline, p. 514)

275. A. Wheezes result from bronchoconstriction, which is small airway narrowing. (Ref. Caroline, p. 181)

276. B. Abdominal or diaphragmatic breathing has chest movements restricted to the abdomen. The strong muscles of the abdomen are used to help pull the diaphragm down. (Ref. Brady, p. 87)

277. C. A cricothyrotomy is indicated when intubation will be difficult or time consuming and the need for airway maintenance is critical. This most often occurs with facial or tracheal trauma. (Ref. Caroline, p. 237)

278. D. Kussmaul's respirations are seen most often in diabetic ketoacidosis and represent an attempt to correct metabolic acidosis with a respiratory alkalosis. They are continuous deep sighing respirations. (Ref. Caroline, p. 619)

279. 1–B, 2–A, 3–D, 4–C. (Ref. Caroline, pp. 197–201)

280. Auscultation of breath sounds. The best verification of tube placement is the sweet sight of the two cords as the tube slides through them. Unfortunately, in our field environment, we cannot depend upon this for many reasons. Likewise, the legal profession would feel that the best verification of tube position is a chest X-ray, since it can be seen by all and provides a timeless verification that tube position was once appropriate. Unfortunately, field X-ray machines are not well developed in EMS systems and often not available during the cardiac arrest. The most repeatable verification, repeatable by any who care to listen, is auscultation. Sounds should be auscultated about at least two positions on each side of the chest and one site over the stomach during inspiration. (Ref. ACLS, p. 32)

281. Protection from aspiration; positive-pressure ventilation; enhancement of ability to deliver higher concentrations of oxygen; ease of airway maintenance; removal of secretions or foreign substances. Intubation is the single best way of securing the airway both for administration of oxygen and positive-pressure ventilation and for prevention of the complications of aspiration. (Ref. ACLS, p. 30)

282. Laceration of lips; avulsion of teeth; laceration of posterior pharynx; avulsion of the arytenoid cartilage; laceration of cords;

perforation of trachea; tracheal stenosis; esophageal intubation; hypoxia during intubation; arrhythmias during intubation — to name a few. Intubation is not innocuous, and every experienced practitioner has his or her horror stories about complications associated with intubation, not just missing an insertion. (Ref. ACLS, p. 32)

283. E. A – D are all accepted indications for emergent intubation for airway control or protection. Normally, the unconscious patient with an intact gag reflex need not be intubated, unless significant other pathology exists. (Ref. Caroline, pp. 226–228; ACLS, p. 30)

284. B. The two cords should be seen before insertion of an endotracheal tube in most cases. All other methods are fraught with the hazard of the missed intubation. (Ref. Caroline, p. 229)

285. E. Listed are all contraindications of the procedure. (Ref. Caroline, p. 233)

286. E. All of these are complications of insertion of an endotracheal tube. (Ref. Caroline, pp. 232–234)

287. C. Hopefully, a laryngoscope is not needed for an EOA insertion. After all, the EOA was designed to eliminate the need for that equipment. (Ref. Caroline, pp. 232–234)

288. C. Increased flexion makes endotrachial intubation with the EOA more likely. (Ref. Caroline, pp. 232–234)

289. A. This question requires a little thought. Anytime the patient is undergoing positive pressure ventilation, there is a chance for a tension pneumothorax. It is particularly common when the patient has had the mucous plugging and bronchoconstriction of asthma. The other items listed are simply not causes of abrupt worsening of the patient's condition in asthma. (Ref. Caroline, p. 200)

290. B. The three lines of defense for the regulation of pH are the acid – base buffer system, the respiratory system, and the renal system. The acid–base buffer system acts essentially instantaneously, but may rapidly be depleted of buffering compounds. (Ref. Grant, pp. 140, 141; Caroline, pp. 65–66)

291. B. Please see comment on Question 290. (Ref. Grant, p. 140; Caroline, pp. 65–66)

292. C. When body fluids are in acid–base balance, the pH is about 7.35 to 7.45. (Ref. Grant, p. 140; Caroline, p. 66)

293. B. Of course, if there is no respiration and no circulation, both metabolic and respiratory acidosis will result. (Ref. ACLS, pp. 129–130)

294. C. In answer C, there is both an increase in the Pco_2, and a decrease in the expected pH. This means that both metabolic acidosis and respiratory acidosis are present. (Ref. ACLS, p. 131)

295. B. Sea-level Pco or partial pressure of carbon dioxide for arterial blood is 40; in Denver, 35–40. (Ref. Grant, p. 138, Caroline, p. 172)

296. D. Normal arterial (sea level) Po_2 or oxygen partial pressure is about 105. It declines by about 5–10 mm Hg per decade over age 40. As the altitude increases, this also decreases—Colorado Springs has a normal Po_2 of about 85. (Ref. Grant, p. 138; Caroline, p. 172)

297. D. At high altitude, the Po_2 is lowered, because of the lowered ambient oxygen tension at lower atmospheric pressure. This causes a reflex hyperventilation and lower Pco_2. pH may or may not change. (Ref. ACLS, p. 131)

298. E. Alcohol intoxication will normally cause respiratory depression, not hyperventilation. Cyanide intoxication, diabetic ketoacidosis, and vigorous exercise will cause metabolic acidosis, with a compensatory hyperventilation. The acute stress reaction produces the hyperventilation syndrome. The important thing to remember is that hyperventilation is also a symptom that may indicate an underlying serious disease. (Ref. Caroline, p. 170)

299. A. The P_{CO_2} is elevated, signifying a respiratory acidosis. (Ref. ACLS, p. 131)

300. B. The pH is depressed, and the P_{CO_2} is also depressed showing an attempt at respiratory compensation. (Ref. ACLS, p. 131)

301. C. The pH is elevated, hence alkalosis. The P_{CO_2} is low, hence respiratory alkalosis. (Ref. ACLS, p. 131)

302. D. This is a profound metabolic acidosis. The only listed etiology that leads to metabolic acidosis is anaerobic metabolism. (Ref. ACLS, p. 130)

303. B. The initial loading dose of bicarbonate should be about 1 mEq/kg. This patient weighs about 50 kg; hence 50 mEq should be given. Standard infusions of bicarbonate contain 1 mEq/mL. (Ref. ACLS, p. 131)

304. B. The very best management is of course use of blood gases to guide our acid–base therapy. Unfortunately, in the field, this is not always possible; perhaps with future technology it will be. Until then, about every 10 minutes, we should consider giving bicarbonate. (Ref. ACLS, p. 265)

305. A. Respiratory alkalosis results when the patient hyperventilates. Metabolic acidosis is the result of ketoacidosis or lactic acidosis among other causes, while metabolic alkalosis would result from an overdose of sodium bicarbonate. Respiratory acidosis is sometimes seen when the patient is unable to properly exchange carbon dioxide in the lungs, as in a patient with COPD. (Ref. Caroline, pp. 175, 215, 422; ACLS, p. 131)

306. C. The classic cause of respiratory alkalosis is hyperventilation. Administering too much bicarbonate during resuscitation is the most important cause of metabolic alkalosis in the paramedic's usual experience. (Ref. Caroline, pp. 175, 215, 422; ACLS, p. 131)

307. A. If the system is producing carbon dioxide at a fixed rate, then elimination is proportional to minute volume. (Minute volume = rate times tidal volume.) Administration of either epinephrine or sodium bicarbonate can be expected to increase the rate of carbon dioxide elimination (by different mechanisms, of course). (Ref. Caroline, p. 173)

308. E. The only condition listed that leads to a metabolic acidosis is diabetic ketoacidosis. All other conditions lead to either respiratory acidosis or respiratory or metabolic alkalosis. (Ref. Caroline, p. 69)

309. A. Hyperventilation will cause a respiratory alkalosis. (Ref. Caroline, p. 69)

310. B. Since respiratory acidosis is caused by decreased respirations, it may be corrected by hyperventilation. (Ref. Grant, p. 141; Caroline, p. 68)

311. D. Hypoventilation is defined as a high Pco_2, in this case, markedly elevated. (Ref. Caroline, pp. 177, 178)

7 Cardiac and Advanced Cardiac Life Support

QUESTIONS 312–341: Select the ONE most appropriate answer.

General

312. In the adult, which of the following usually discharges (at rest) 60 to 100 times per minute?
    A. Bachmann's bundle
    B. Wenckebach's bundle
    C. Atrioventricular node
    D. Sinoatrial node
    E. Node of His

313. The location of the heart, with the right ventricle positioned just posterior to the sternum, is the
    A. manubrium
    B. mediastinum
    C. mydriasis
    D. mesentery
    E. miasma

314. As blood is ejected from the right ventricle, through which arteries, veins, and capillaries does the blood pass on its way into the left ventricle?
   A. Hepatic
   B. Renal
   C. Pulmonary
   D. Coronary
   E. Mediastinal

315. Through what valve is blood ejected when leaving the right ventricle?
   A. Aortic
   B. Mitral
   C. Pulmonic
   D. Tricuspid
   E. Antral

316. Venous blood drains, via the coronary sinus, into the
   A. superior vena cava
   B. inferior vena cava
   C. right pulmonary artery
   D. left atrium
   E. right atrium

317. The heart cannot utilize blood from within its chambers for oxygen; therefore, it must pump blood into the aorta and coronary circulation. Approximately what percentage of the cardiac output is found in the coronary circulation?
   A. 1
   B. 5
   C. 9
   D. 12
   E. 17

318. The heart valves
    A. permit unidirectional blood flow
    B. are opened and closed by action of the papillary muscles
    C. open passively and close mainly by ventricular blood flow
    D. A and C
    E. A–D

319. The right atrioventricular valve
    A. has three flaps of endocardium
    B. has only two endocardial flaps
    C. is known as the tricuspid valve
    D. is known as the mitral valve
    E. A and C

320. The left atrioventricular valve
    A. has three flaps of endocardium
    B. is known as the mitral valve
    C. is known as the tricuspid valve
    D. is known as the quadricuspid valve
    E. A and C

321. Pacemaker rates in the heart are
    A. fastest in the SA node
    B. fastest in the AV node
    C. fastest in the His–Purkinje system
    D. fastest in the ventricle
    E. uniform throughout the heart

322. The myocardial cell's inability to be depolarized at a given instant is known as
    A. automaticity
    B. refractoriness
    C. reentry
    D. rhythmicity
    E. erogenicity

323. What are the three arteries branching off the aortic arch?
   1. Subclavian
   2. Brachiocephalic
   3. Common carotid
   4. Brachial
      A. 2,3, and 4
      B. 1,2, and 4
      C. 1,2, and 3
      D. 1,3, and 4

324. If a patient's heart rate increases, but stroke volume remains the same, cardiac output will
   A. increase
   B. decrease
   C. remain the same

325. Which procedures are appropriate for the patient with cardiac pulmonary edema?
   1. Administering oxygen
   2. Placing the patient in a sitting position
   3. Placing an elastic bandage around the chest to reduce congestion
   4. Placing the patient supine with the lower extremities elevated at a 15° angle
      A. 2 only
      B. 1 and 2
      C. 1 and 3
      D. 1 and 4
      E. All of the above

326. Pulmonary edema can be caused or made worse by
   A. myocardial infarction
   B. arrhythmias
   C. fluid overload
   D. propranolol
   E. all of the above

327. Where is atrial repolarization shown on an ECG?
   A. In the ST segment
   B. In the P wave
   C. In the T wave
   D. Buried in the QRS complex
   E. Between T and subsequent P waves (U wave)

328. You respond to a call for a patient in chest pain. While obtaining a history, you learn that this patient has had angina for the last 2 years. Lately, however, the chest pain has increased in frequency, severity, and duration, and seems unrelated to stress. It is now associated with nausea. These symptoms indicate
   A. preinfarction angina (unstable angina)
   B. hiatal hernia
   C. stable angina
   D. upper respiratory infection
   E. acute pulmonary infarction

329. Which is not a symptom of cardiac tamponade?
   A. Distant heart sounds
   B. Ankle edema
   C. Distended neck veins
   D. Increased diastolic BP, decreased systolic BP
   E. Shock

330. What is the major vein that drains the blood from the legs and abdomen into the right atrium?
   A. Inferior vena cava
   B. Femoral vein
   C. Superior vena cava
   D. Pulmonary vein
   E. Innominate veins

331. Which is not a sign of hemopericardium?
   A. Shock
   B. Hypertension
   C. Increased jugular venous pressure (distended neck veins)
   D. Narrowing pulse pressure
   E. Muffled or distant heart sounds

332. What is NOT a factor strongly associated with the development of ventricular fibrillation?
- **A.** Acute myocardial infarction
- **B.** Transient myocardial ischemia
- **C.** Underlying cardiomyopathy
- **D.** Scar tissue from a prior myocardial infarction
- **E.** Elevated cholesterol

333. Which is true for the majority of patients who suffer sudden cardiac death?
- **A.** They have no premonitory symptoms immediately prior to collapse.
- **B.** Sudden cardiac death may be the first manifestation in up to 20% of all patients with heart disease.
- **C.** They have no infarction per se.
- **D.** They die outside the hospital.
- **E.** All of the above.

334. Which of the following is NOT a symptom of an acute myocardial infarction or impending sudden cardiac death?
- **A.** New onset of crushing substernal chest pain
- **B.** New onset of tachypnea and left lateral pleuritic chest pain
- **C.** A change in a previously stable pattern of angina
- **D.** An increase in the frequency of anginal attacks
- **E.** Heartburn, nausea, vomiting, and weakness

335. When is the most common time of onset of a myocardial infarction?
- **A.** Noon to 6 PM
- **B.** 6 PM to midnight
- **C.** Midnight to 6 AM
- **D.** 6 AM to noon
- **E.** Myocardial infarctions do not occur at any particular time; they tend to occur uniformly throughout the day.

336. When is an individual with myocardial infarction most at risk for ventricular fibrillation found?
    A. In the first hour after a myocardial infarction
    B. During the first 12 hours after a myocardial infarction
    C. 24 hours after the myocardial infarction
    D. 3 days after the myocardial infarction
    E. 6 weeks after the myocardial infarction

337. Which of the following agents is NOT indicated in the treatment of pulmonary edema associated with an myocardial infarction?
    A. Isoproterenol
    B. Morphine sulfate
    C. Furosemide
    D. Intravenous nitroprusside
    E. Nitroglycerin

338. Which of the following conditions would NOT be mistaken for an acute myocardial infarction?
    A. Aortic dissection
    B. Splenic rupture
    C. Cardiac tamponade
    D. Septic shock
    E. Pulmonary embolism

339. What is NOT a commonly occurring mechanism for bradycardia in the setting of an acute myocardial infarction?
    A. Hypertrophic heart
    B. Sinus bradycardia
    C. Junctional escape rhythm
    D. Increased parasympathetic tone
    E. Second- or third-degree heart block

340. What pathological conditions have been associated with the development of an acute myocardial infarction?
    A. Cocaine abuse
    B. Hypertensive heart disease
    C. Diabetes
    D. Emotional stress
    E. All of the above

341. Cardiac arrest is the first manifestation of heart disease in what percentage of patients?
- **A.** 20
- **B.** 36
- **C.** 48
- **D.** 67
- **E.** 73

QUESTION 342: Number the list of lettered items in the correct order, from 1 to 9.

---

342. Starting with the venous circulation, order the following structures to show blood flow through the heart.
- **A.** _____ Pulmonary vein
- **B.** _____ Left atrium
- **C.** _____ Aorta
- **D.** _____ Vena cavae
- **E.** _____ Pulmonary artery
- **F.** _____ Left ventricle
- **G.** _____ Right atrium
- **H.** _____ Pulmonary capillaries
- **I.** _____ Right ventricle

QUESTIONS 343-348: Fill in the appropriate words or phrases.

---

343. What are six major factors predisposing individuals to sudden cardiac death?
- **1.** _____
- **2.** _____
- **3.** _____
- **4.** _____
- **5.** _____
- **6.** _____

Defibrillation and Cardioversion

344. How many joules should be applied in the initial defibrillation attempt?

_____

345. If the first attempt at defibrillation is unsuccessful, how many joules should be applied at the second try?

_____

346. What are four patient-related factors that can affect transthoracic impedance?

1. _____
2. _____
3. _____
4. _____

347. What paddle size is recommended for each of these patients?

Infants _____
Older child _____
Adult _____

348. What are three safety precautions that should be remembered during use of the defibrillator?

1. _____
2. _____
3. _____

QUESTIONS 349–384: Select the ONE most appropriate answer.

349. Which arrhythmia can be best treated by pacing?
    1. Ventricular fibrillation
    2. Ventricular tachycardia
    3. Ventricular asystole
    4. High-grade block (complete heart block)
        A. 1 and 2
        B. 3 and 4
        C. 1, 2, and 4
        E. All of the above

350. If it is necessary to shock a patient with a permanent pacemaker, how far from the pacemaker generator should the paddles be placed?
    A. 1 in.
    B. 3 in.
    C. 4 in.
    D. 5 in.
    E. 8 in.

351. To reduce impedance when defibrillating, it is best to use
    A. alcohol pads
    B. lubricating jelly
    C. saline-soaked gauze pads
    D. electrode paste
    E. benzoin

352. To ensure maximum delivery of current from a defibrillation attempt,
    1. some conductive material should be used between the paddles and the patient's chest
    2. there should be as much patient–paddle contact as possible
    3. the charge given the patient should always be the maximum the defibrillator can offer
    4. the patient and paramedic should be on a dry surface
    A. 2 and 3
    B. 2, 3, and 4
    C. 1, 3, and 4
    D. 1, 2, and 4
    E. 1 and 2

Dysrhythmias

353. You are called to see a 68-year-old clerk in a department store who "stumbled." You find that the patient's pulse is 30, the blood pressure is 70/50, and the patient is incoherent (Figure 1). This rhythm represents
    A. sinus bradycardia
    B. third-degree AV (complete) heart block
    C. Mobitz type I (Wenckebach) heart block
    D. Mobitz type II (2:1) heart block
    E. atrial fibrillation with a slow ventricular response

Figure 1.

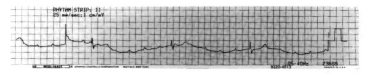

354. The appropriate therapy for this dysrhythmia is
  A. atropine and dobutamine
  B. atropine and pacemaker
  C. sodium bicarbonate and lidocaine
  D. lidocaine and dobutamine
  E. lidocaine and MAST

355. Identify the dysrhythmia in Figure 2.
  A. Mobitz type II block
  B. Atrial flutter
  C. Atrial fibrillation
  D. Third-degree heart block
  E. Muscle tremor

356. Your next patient is a 56-year-old account executive for a large advertising firm that specializes in tobacco ads. He is a frequent user of his client's products. Today he was notified of a Supreme Court decision that allows consumers to sue both the advertising firm and the tobacco firm for "harmful" advertising. He now has a tightness in his chest, together with some nausea. His secretary has called your service. His blood pressure is 124/96, with 22 respirations per minute (Figure 3). This rhythm represents
  A. sinus bradycardia
  B. third-degree AV (complete) heart block
  C. multifocal premature ventricular contractions
  D. unifocal premature ventricular contractions
  E. atrial fibrillation with a slow ventricular response

Figure 2.

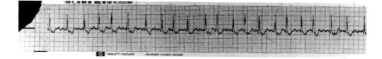

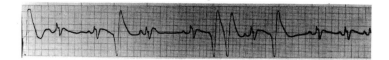

Figure 3.

357. Immediate therapy of this dysrhythmia should be
   A. oxygen
   B. lidocaine
   C. atropine
   D. epinephrine
   E. bretylium

358. Identify the rhythm in Figure 4.
   A. Artifact
   B. Ventricular fibrillation
   C. Multifocal PVCs
   D. Pacemaker-induced rhythm
   E. Ventricular tachycardia

359. Important steps in the management of a pulseless patient
   with the rhythm shown in Figure 5 include
   1. rapid fluid challenge with normal saline
   2. evaluation of breath sounds and chest excursion
   3. infusion of epinephrine 0.5 mgs
   4. verapamil 5 mg intravenously
      A. 1, 2, and 3
      B. 1 and 3
      C. 2 and 4
      D. 4 only
      E. All of the above

Figure 4.

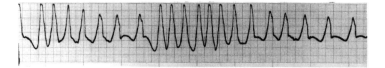

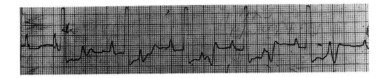

Figure 5.

360. You are called to a bar, where you find a 43-year-old woman who has collapsed on the floor. As you evaluate the patient, you find the rhythm shown in Figure 6. What is the R – R wave interval?
   A. Irregular
   B. 0.2 second
   C. 0.4 second
   D. 0.8 second
   E. It cannot be determined

361. This rhythm is called
   A. sinus rhythm with multiple PACs
   B. atrial fibrillation
   C. atrial flutter
   D. baseline artifact
   E. ventricular fibrillation

362. Your immediate treatment should be
   A. defibrillation at 200 watt-seconds
   B. defibrillation at 50 watt-seconds
   C. synchronized cardioversion at 200 watt-seconds
   D. 10 mg of verapamil intravenously
   E. CPR and administration of 0.5 mg of atropine

Figure 6.

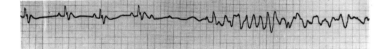

363. You are called to see an account executive in a local stock broker's office just after a "market readjustment." You find a pale sweating man about 50, with nausea and crushing substernal chest pain. On monitoring the patient, you get the rhythm shown in Figure 7. This rhythm represents
    A. ventricular fibrillation
    B. Mobitz type I (Wenckebach)
    C. Mobitz type II (2:1 block)
    D. third-degree heart block

364. This rhythm is important because
    A. it may revert to a complete heart block
    B. it may revert to a ventricular fibrillation
    C. it may cause significant hypertension
    D. it may cause ventricular tachycardia
    E. it is predictive of final extent of infarct size

365. The leading cause of death in a patient with an acute myocardial infarction is
    A. hypoxia
    B. CHF
    C. arrhythmia
    D. pulmonary embolus
    E. cardiogenic shock

366. Certain cells of the myocardium are capable of generating and conducting electrical activity, causing depolarization and contraction. This property is called
    A. myocardiogenesis
    B. homeostasis
    C. automaticity
    D. polarity
    E. contractility

Figure 7.

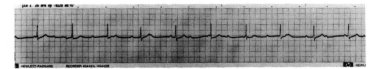

367. Ventricular fibrillation
  1. can be mimicked by artifact on the oscilloscope
  2. can occur in the presence of a peripheral pulse
  3. decreases effective cardiac output
  4. should be treated with CPR and defibrillation
    A. 1 and 3
    B. 1, 2, and 4
    C. 1, 3, and 4
    D. 4 only
    E. all of the above

368. Pacemaker cells are located in the
  A. atrium, the bundle of His
  B. ventricles, the Purkinje fibers
  C. AV node
  D. all of the above

369. Which part of the ECG represents depolarization of the atrium?
  A. QRS
  B. T wave
  C. P wave
  D. U wave
  E. S-T segment

370. What portion of the ECG shows repolarization of the ventricle?
  A. QRS
  B. T wave
  C. P wave
  D. U wave
  E. S-T segment

371. The upper limit of the normal P-R interval is
  A. 0.1 second
  B. 0.2 second
  C. 1.0 second
  D. 0.12 second
  E. 0.3 second

372. The upper limit to the normal duration of the QRS is
    A. 0.012 second
    B. 0.12 second
    C. 0.30 second
    D. 0.25 second
    E. 0.6 second

373. What methods can be used to determine heart rate?
    1. Count P waves for 10 seconds and multiply by 6.
    2. Count P waves for 30 seconds and multiply by 2.
    3. Count P waves for 60 seconds.
    4. Count QRS complexes for 60 seconds.
        A. 1 and 3
        B. 1 and 2
        C. All of the above
        D. None of the above

374. Atrial fibrillation is treated with
    1. verapamil
    2. β-blocking agents
    3. digitalis derivatives
    4. vagal maneuvers
        A. 1 and 3
        B. 2 and 4
        C. 4 only
        D. 1, 2, and 3
        E. all of the above

375. What type of pause usually follows a PVC (premature ventricular contraction)?
    A. Compensatory
    B. Noncompensatory
    C. Paradoxical
    D. Eliminatory
    E. Vagal

376. Ventricular tachycardia occurs when
    A. 1 or more beats of ventricular origin occur at a rate of 150 or more per minute
    B. 2 or more beats of ventricular origin occur at a rate of 100 or more per minute
    C. 5 or more beats of ventricular origin occur at a rate of 120 or more per minute
    D. 3 or more beats of ventricular origin occur at a rate of 100 or more per minute

377. Treatment for first-degree AV block includes
    1. IV D₅W TKO
    2. O₂ at 2–4 L/min by nasal cannula
    3. monitoring the patient's ECG
    4. lidocaine 1 mg/kg IV push
    5. atopine 0.5 mg IV push
        A. 1, 2, and 3
        B. 2, 3, and 4
        C. 1, 2, 3, and 4
        D. 1, 2, 3, and 5

378. Sudden death is most frequently due to which of these rhythm disturbances
    A. Fig. 8a
    B. Fig. 8b
    C. Fig. 8c
    D. Fig. 8d
    E. Fig. 8e

Figure 8a.

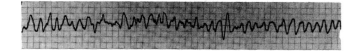

Figure 8b.

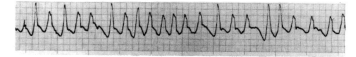

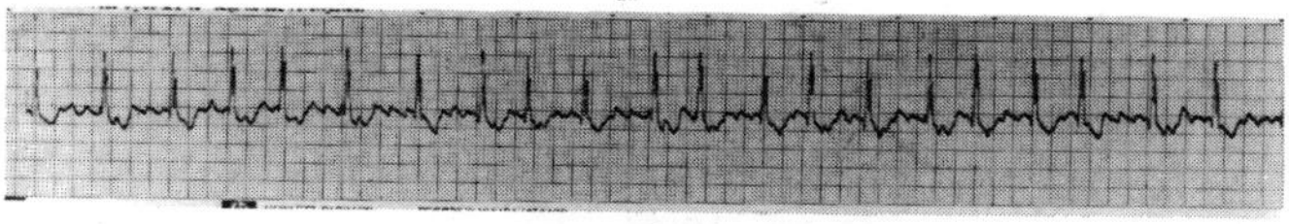

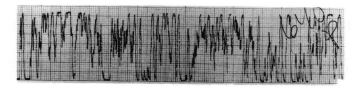

Figure 8c.

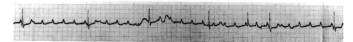

Figure 8d.

Figure 8e.

379. The correct dosage of atropine for a cardiac patient with a
bradycardia of 30 and hypotension is
    A. 0.5 mg IV push, repeated every 5 minutes to a total
        dose of 2.0 mg or until appropriate effect (whichever
        comes first)
    B. 5 mg IV bolus
    C. 5 – 7 mg/kg IV push
    D. 50 cc IV push followed by 1 – 2 g in 250 – 500 cc D_5W
    E. 0.5 mg intramuscularly

380. The spontaneous initiation of depolarizing impulses by the
pacemaker sites within the myocardial electrical conduction
system is called
    A. the refractory period
    B. automaticity
    C. Frank Starling's law
    D. contractibility
    E. excitability

381. You are treating a patient with a blood pressure of 80/50. His pulse is 120, and the neck veins are distended. This patient is complaining of chest pain but there is no evidence of trauma. He is anxious, cold, and clammy, and his respiratory rate is 26. Breath sounds are present in all lung fields. Which order would you anticipate?
    A. Begin CPR
    B. Do nothing
    C. Give 0.5 atropine IV bolus
    D. Start a dopamine drip
    E. Needle thoracotomy aspiration (venting) of the right chest

382. Which order would be appropriate for a patient with a pulse of 68 and about 10 multifocal PVCs per minute, who is complaining of chest pain?
    A. Cardioversion at 50 watt-seconds (joules)
    B. Lidocaine bolus of 1 mg/kg
    C. Dopamine drip at 5 μg/kg/min
    D. 0.5 to 1 mg atropine IV bolus
    E. Epinephrine 0.01 mg/kg bolus

383. Which order would you expect for a patient with a Mobitz type II rhythm? This patient has a pulse of 52 and blood pressure of 126/74.
    A. Monitor and transport
    B. Give lidocaine bolus of 1 mg/kg
    C. Give 0.5 to 1 mg atropine IV bolus
    D. Start a dopamine drip at 5 μg/kg/min
    E. Give 0.01 mg/kg of epinephrine

384. You note that your patient is conscious, but has signs and symptoms of shock such as clammy skin and mottled color. Her pulse is 200 and weak and thready. The monitor shows ventricular tachycardia. Thump-cardioversion fails. Which order should you anticipate?
    A. Monitor and transport
    B. Give bretylium bolus of 5 mg/kg
    C. Give 0.5 to 1 mg atropine IV bolus
    D. Start a dopamine drip at 5 μg/kg/min
    E. Cardiovert at 50 watt-seconds (joules)

QUESTIONS 385–395: Answer *True* or *False*.

385. Always treat bradycardias of less than 60 beats per minute in the patient with an acute myocardial infarction.
True
False

386. Sinus tachycardia is commonly associated with an acute myocardial infarction.
True
False

387. Use of an artificial pacemaker is urgently required for most cases of Mobitz type I heart blocks associated with acute myocardial infarction.
True
False

388. It is best to use Lidocaine in the treatment of a Mobitz type II second-degree heart block that follows an inferior wall infarction.
True
False

389. Atrial fibrillation or bundle branch block that develops early in the course of an acute myocardial infarction is associated with increased mortality.
True
False

390. During the refractory period, another electrical impulse cannot occur.
True
False

391. An escape pacemaker is a transvenous pacemaker whose leads have escaped their normal site of embedding in the myocardium.
True
False

392. The P–R interval represents the beginning of atrial depolarization to the end of ventricular repolarization.
True
False

393. In all cases, acute myocardial infarction presents with a low normal or low blood pressure in addition to the other symptoms.
True
False

394. Low blood pressure, low pulmonary capillary wedge pressure, and low cardiac output characterize the cardiogenic shock associated with acute myocardial infarction.
True
False

395. The QRS interval represents the onset of ventricular depolarization.
True
False

QUESTIONS 396 and 397: Fill in the appropriate word or phrase.

396. What is the criterion for a Sinus Tachycardia?

_____

397. What is the criterion for a Sinus Bradycardia?

_____

Explanatory Answers

312. D. In the average resting adult, the sinoatrial node is the primary pacemaker of the heart, discharging 60–100 times per minute. (Ref. Grant, p. 199; Caroline, pp. 279–281)

313. B. The heart is located in the mediastinum (middle of the chest). (Ref. Grant, p. 173; Caroline, p. 621)

314. C. The pulmonary arteries are the only arteries that carry deoxygenated blood (from the heart to the lungs). (Ref. Grant, p. 174; Caroline, p. 31)

315. C. Blood is ejected through the right ventricle to the pulmonic valve, to the pulmonary artery, etc. (Ref. Grant, p. 174; Caroline, p. 30)

316. E. The venous blood drains into the right atrium via the coronary sinus. [This is not covered in Nancy Caroline's book.] (Ref. Grant, p. 175)

317. B. The heart is a muscle that requires a substantial part of the heart's output to continue living! (Ref. Grant, p. 174)

318. A. The heart valves permit unidirectional blood flow as a result of being opened by blood pressure and held closed by the papillary muscles, which keep the leaflets of the valves from backflow. This is not well covered in Caroline's test. (Ref. Grant, p. 237; Caroline, p. 252)

319. E. The right atrioventricular valve, also known as the tricuspid valve, has three flaps of endocardium. Although Caroline does not mention specifically the three flaps of endocardium, "tricuspid" = three cusps or flaps. (Ref. Grant, p. 146; Caroline, p. 252)

320. B. The mitral valve, known as such for the mitre shape (like a bishop's hat), is the left atrioventricular valve. (Ref. Grant, p. 174; Caroline, p. 252)

321. A. In the normal heart, the dominant pacemaker is the SA node, normally firing at a rate of 60 – 100 times per minute. (Ref. Caroline, p. 257)

322. B. The period when the heart is unable to be depolarized is the refractory period. (Ref. Caroline, p. 257)

323. C. The brachial artery, which is in the arm, has branched from the subclavian to the axillary to the brachial artery. (Ref. Caroline, p. 31, Fig. 2 – 14)

324. A. As cardiac output equals stroke volume times heart rate, increasing the heart rate increases cardiac output. (Ref. Caroline, p. 255)

325. B. It makes little sense to elevate the legs and increase the circulating vascular volume in a patient overloaded with fluids; hence 4 is wrong. It never makes sense to interfere with respirations; hence 3 is wrong. (Ref. Caroline, p. 269)

326. E. Fluid overload, dysrhythmias (particularly common with atrial fibrillation), and myocardial infarctions are common causes of pulmonary edema. Pulmonary edema can be worsened by the β-blocking action of propranolol with its subsequent decreased output. (Ref. Caroline, pp. 155, 270)

327. D. This is actually a bit tricky. The T wave represents repolarization of the *ventricles*. The P wave represents *depolarization* of the atria. The ST segment and U waves are too late in the cycle to represent repolarization of the normal atria; hence the atrial repolarization must be buried in the QRS complex. (Ref. ACLS, p. 49)

328. A. Unstable angina is a hallmark of the impending myocardial infarction. Anytime a patient requires three or more nitroglycerin tablets to relieve angina over a period of 15 minutes, a myocardial infarction should be suspected. (Ref. ACLS, p. 11)

329. B. Ankle edema is a symptom of heart failure, not of cardiac tamponade. Ankle edema develops over days to weeks, whereas cardiac tamponade develops over hours. (Ref. Caroline, p. 274)

330. A. The inferior vena cava drains all of the blood below the diaphragm into the heart. (Ref. Caroline, p. 31)

331. B. Cardiac tamponade gives you hypotension not hypertension. (Ref. Caroline, p. 274)

332. In the overwhelming majority of patients who suffer sudden cardiac death, a prior coronary artery or ischemic heart disease is present. In the rest, cardiomyopathy, valvular heart disease, or hypertension can account for the abnormality. Elevated cholesterol predisposes to heart disease in general, but not specifically to ventricular fibrillation.

333. The majority of patients who die suddenly from heart disease do so without any premonitory symptoms, outside of the hospital, and have no infarction. It is the first manifestation of disease in up to 20% of those suffering from heart disease. Up to 1,000 persons die this way each day in the United States. (Ref. ACLS, p. 3)

334. B. Tachypnea and pleuritic chest pain should make you think of a pulmonary embolus, not a myocardial infarction. Although "indigestion" is not a common pattern for a myocardial infarction, any unusual or prolonged indigestion should raise suspicions. (Ref. ACLS, p. 11)

335. D. There is a marked increase in the incidence of myocardial infarctions from 6 AM to noon. The reasons for this increase are not yet understood. (Ref. ACLS, p. 11)

336. A. The most risk for an individual with a myocardial infarction is within the first hour after the infarction. Indeed, ventricular fibrillation is fifteen times more common during the first hour than it is during the subsequent 12 hours. (Ref. ACLS, p. 12)

337. A. Isoproterenol will markedly increase the myocardial oxygen consumption. This is not a beneficial effect in the setting of the myocardial infarction. (Ref. ACLS, p. 17)

338. B. Hopefully, splenic rupture should cause abdominal signs and symptoms that will distinguish it from the thoracic causes listed. Septic and anaphylactic shock may cause a marked reduction in the systemic vascular resistance and are easily confused with a myocardial infarction in the elderly. (Ref. ACLS, p. 19)

339. A. Bradycardia is most often seen in the first hour after a myocardial infarction. Common mechanisms include the second- and third-degree blocks, junctional escape rhythms, and sinus bradycardia. Most of the time these rhythms are due to an increase in the parasympathetic or vagal tone. They are usually associated with inferior or posterior myocardial infarctions. The hypertrophic heart of the athlete that causes bradycardia is not usually seen as an acute event. (Ref. ACLS, p. 13)

340. B. All of these pathological conditions have been associated with development of acute myocardial infarction. It is interesting that the marked disparity in oxygen supply and demand associated with cocaine abuse can precipitate a myocardial infarction in even 20-year-olds. (Ref. ACLS, p. 11)

341. A. As well as we do, cardiac arrest is still the cause in many unexpected deaths. Unfortunately, in up to 20% of patients, the FIRST manifestation of disease is death. (Ref. ACLS, p. 2)

342. A—6, B—7, C—9, D—1, E—8, F—4, G—2, H—5, I—3.

343. Male sex, old age, high blood cholesterol, diabetes mellitus, hypertension, exercise, history of atherosclerosis, cigarette smoking. (Ref. ACLS, p. 3)

344. 200. A patient in ventricular fibrillation has a better chance of survival if defibrillated quickly. The initial and first subsequent attempt at defibrillation should usually be at 200 joules. The third attempt is made at 360 joules. The size of the patient needs to be considered when calculating the energy requirement for defibrillation; an extremely large person may require more energy on the original attempt than a much smaller and thinner person. (Ref. ACLS, p. 238)

345. 200–300. Most authorities suggest that the second countershock be at the same power as the first, 200 joules. Again, this countershock should not be delayed for intubation, insertion of intravenous line, or other interventions. (Ref. ACLS, p. 238)

346. Delivered energy, repetitive shocks, paddle size and composition, phase of patient's ventilation, paddle placement (interelectrode distance), temperature of patient, patient's heart size. In defibrillation, transthoracic impedance is affected by the placement, size, and composition of the paddles and those characteristics that make up the patient, such as size of chest and heart, internal chemistry, and temperature. Repetitive shocks also decrease transthoracic impedance. (Ref. ACLS, pp. 90–92)

347. Infant—4.5 cm; child—8 cm; adult—13 cm. Remember that paddle electrode size varies according to the patient's size. The optimum size for adults is probably about 13 cm. (Ref. ACLS, pp. 91–92)

348. Working place should be dry, "clear" area prior to discharge, discharge paddles when not needed, do not lean on the paddles as they may slip as you defibrillate. The defibrillator is not an innocuous machine and is dangerous to the operator and bystanders, if not used properly. (Ref. ACLS, p. 92)

349. B. Pacing may be tried for complete heart block and aystole, whereas defibrillation may be used to convert ventricular tachycardia or fibrillation to a useful rhythm. (Ref. ACLS, p. 242)

350. D. The proper answer should be "as far as possible from the pacemaker," but this is not always practical. Five inches represents a compromise, given chest size and defibrillator paddle size. The pacemaker leads may conduct the defibrillation shock, causing local burns and increasing the current requirement for effective pacing. (Ref. ACLS, p. 95)

351. D. The best solution may be the prewrapped gel pad, which leaves no mess, is easily removable, and does not cause the person performing chest compressions to slip. Alternatively, electrode paste will suffice and is also recommended, but should be wiped off between defibrillations to decrease the arcing potential and allow for more effective compressions. Alcohol-soaked pads are flammable and not appropriate, whereas saline-soaked pads may cause arcing and dissipation of the transmitted charge. (Ref. ACLS, p. 91)

352. D. Although it is wise to ensure that the patient is on a dry surface, this has little to do with DELIVERY of current to the patient. Greater paddle–patient contact and a conductive material will increase the delivered current, however. (Ref. ACLS, p. 91; Caroline, p. 332)

353. B. In a third-degree block, there is relationship between P waves and the QRS complexes. The QRS complexes are usually bizarre and are often wide because of the location of the spontaneous pacemaker. As P waves are present, this cannot be an atrial fibrillation. (Ref. Caroline, p. 296; ACLS, p. 242)

354. B. The appropriate therapy for this condition is a pacemaker, either inserted into the veins or applied to the skin. Atropine and Isuprel will buy time to allow the paramedic to set up the transcutaneous pacer or the hospital to set up the transvenous pacemaker. (Ref. Caroline, p. 296; ACLS, p. 242)

355. B. This rhythm is atrial flutter, recognizable by the presence of regular sawtooth "flutter-waves" at a rate between 240 and 360 per minute. (Ref. ACLS, p. 64; Caroline, p. 292)

356. D. There is only one shape to the premature ventricular contractions, so this must represent only one irritable focus—unifocal. (Ref. Caroline, p. 297; ACLS, p. 74)

357. A. This actually is a bit tricky. IMMEDIATE therapy of this dysrhythmia should be supplemental oxygen by either cannula or face mask, and all patients with a suspected myocardial infarction should be started on oxygen, WHILE the IV is being prepared.

After insertion of an IV, lidocaine is indicated in all patients with suspected myocardial infarction and this rhythm. (Ref. ACLS, p. 243; Caroline, p. 266)

358. E. The rate is greater than 100 with large, wide QRS complexes. This is the picture of ventricular tachycardia. Atrial tachycardia with aberrant conduction pathways may also on occasion simulate ventricular tachycardia. (Ref. ACLS, p. 78; Caroline, p. 299)

359. A. Treatment of the patient with electromechanical dissociation should be centered about correctable disorders. The highest priority, therefore, is a rapid search for correctable lesions, such as tension pneumothorax, hypovolemia, plugged or malpositioned endotracheal tubes, and cardiac tamponade. (Ref. ACLS, 240; Caroline, pp. 328–330)

360. E. Needless to say, in this chaotic rhythm of ventricular fibrillation, there is no R–R wave interval, regular or otherwise. (Ref. Caroline, p. 300; ACLS, p. 79)

361. E. As noted, this is ventricular fibrillation. Artifact must be considered, but if the patient is pulseless and nonresponsive, artifact is unlikely. (Ref. Caroline, p. 300; ACLS, p. 79)

362. A. The most important determination of survival in ventricular fibrillation is rapid defibrillation. The appropriate starting "dose" is 200 joules or watt-seconds. (Ref. Caroline, p. 300; ACLS, p. 238)

363. C. This is a Mobitz type II or second-degree block in a 2:1 pattern. (Ref. Caroline, p. 295; ACLS, p. 82)

364. A. Mobitz type II is important because it may convert to a complete heart block at any time. It is not completely predictive of the extent of infarct, but is often associated with extensive anterior wall myocardial infarctions. Tachycardia and hypertension are NOT associated with this rhythm. (Ref. Caroline, p. 295; ACLS, p. 15)

365. C. In prehospital care, the leading cause of death is certainly dysrhythmias. Even in hospitalized patients, a leading cause of death remains intractable dysrhythmias. (Ref. ACLS, p. 11; Caroline, p. 276)

366. C. Automaticity is the property of causing an electrical stimulus, and subsequent depolarization and contraction of other cells. All myocardial cells have this potential to act as a pacemaker. (Ref. ACLS, p. 45; Caroline, p. 257)

367. C. VF is never associated with an effective pulse because there is not a sufficient organized contracture of the myocardium to cause any pulse. (Ref. ACLS, p. 64; Caroline, p. 300)

368. D. All cardiac fibers are potentially pacemaker cells and can initiate myocardial contraction. (Ref. ACLS, p. 45; Caroline, p. 257)

369. C. Depolarization of the atrium is represented by the P wave, whereas depolarization of the ventricle is represented by the QRS complex. Repolarization of the P wave is usually buried in the QRS complex and is not visible. (Ref. ACLS, p. 49; Caroline, p. 259)

370. B. Repolarization of the ventricle is found in the T wave. Repolarization of the atrium is usually buried in the QRS complex. (Ref. ACLS, p. 49; Caroline, p. 259)

371. B. The PR interval should not exceed 0.2 second or five small squares on ECG paper (1 square = 0.04 second). (Ref. ACLS, p. 49)

372. B. The normal width of the QRS complex is three small squares or less on ECG paper (0.12 second). (Ref. ACLS, p. 49)

373. C. Counting the P waves is appropriate only when there is no atrioventricular conduction block. At that point, counting QRS complexes is more appropriate. (Ref. ACLS, p. 53; Caroline, p. 279)

374. D. Verapamil and vagal maneuvers may slow the heart rate in some patients with accelerated ventricular responses to atrial fibrillation. Digitalis is the standard therapy for decreasing of the heart rate. (Ref. ACLS, p. 245)

375. A. As the rhythm of the sinus node is not disturbed, a compensatory pause follows the premature ventricular contraction. (Ref. ACLS, p. 74)

376. D. Ventricular tachycardia is the presence of three or more beats with a rate greater than 100. These beats originate in ventricular foci and need not be conducted normally. (Ref. ACLS, p. 75)

377. A. First-degree AV block does not require therapy. If it is associated with an acute problem, the patient should be monitored for the development of second- or third-degree heart block. (Ref. ACLS, p. 87)

378. A. Rhythm A is ventricular fibrillation, the most common rhythm noted in cardiac arrests. (Ref. Caroline, pp. 300, 315)

379. A. The best therapy for this condition is electrical pacing with a transcutaneous pacemaker. Atropine will temporize until you can get the patient paced. The maximum atropinizing dose for cardiac purposes is 2.0 mg. For patients with anticholinesterase inhibitor poisoning, far greater quantities may be needed. (Intramuscular injections should not be used for cardiac patients.) (Ref. ACLS, pp. 99–100)

380. B. This is the definition of automaticity. It is a feature of many specialized myocardial muscle fibers (the pacemaker pathway), and is the reason that the patient with a third-degree heart block can survive at all. (Ref. ACLS, p. 45)

381. D. This patient is probably having an acute myocardial infarction. Although this picture may also be seen in the patient with a tension pneumothorax, it is more likely that the patient would have a markedly elevated respiratory rate and some difference in lung sounds. He deserves a trial of sympathomimetics such as dopamine. (Ref. Caroline, pp. 270–271)

382. D. Most authorities would start lidocaine in the presence of multifocal PVCs of more than 6 per minute. The other medications are clearly not indicated and would tend to increase the rate of PVCs, and therefore increase the likelihood of a PVC triggering ventricular fibrillation. (Ref. Caroline, p. 298)

383. A. The appropriate therapy for this patient is likely to be a pacemaker. With a pulse of 56, this is not an emergent therapy, hence the monitor and transport order. (Ref. Caroline, p. 295)

384. E. This is the classic indication for emergent cardioversion: the decompensated ventricular tachycardia patient. A hypotensive patient should be treated as if she is having ventricular fibrillation, with immediate countershock. Lidocaine or another antiarrythmic drug is also certainly indicated. The use of bretylium in this setting is controversial, however, and it is certainly not a standard first-line drug. (Ref. Caroline, p. 299)

385. False. Controversy exists regarding the management of bradycardia during a MI. Investigations of ischemic hearts emphasize the fact that bradycardia rates exert a protective mechanism. In addition, a bradycardia that is asymptomatic, particularly in the athlete, may signify nothing. (Ref. ACLS, p. 13; Caroline, p. 286)

386. False. In a small but significant number of cases, pain or anxiety or both may be responsible for the sinus tachycardia. In that case, analgesia and/or sedation may be all that is required. In many instances, the tachycardia is due to massive myocardial damage or hypovolemia; in these cases β-andrenergic blockade may be contraindicated. (Ref. ACLS, p. 13; Caroline, p. 287)

387. False. Normally, a Mobitz type I (Wenckebach) heart block carries no particular prognostic import. A temporary pacemaker may be necessary only if atropine is not effective or if hemodynamically significant bradycardia recurs. (Ref. ACLS, p. 15; Caroline, p. 294)

388. False. When a second-degree Mobitz type II heart block is associated with infarction, it carries a significant risk of progression to complete heart block. Therefore, it is an indication for placement of a transvenous pacemaker. Lidocaine would exacerbate the block. (Ref. ACLS, p. 15; Caroline, p. 295)

389. True. Development of either a bundle branch block or atrial fibrillation, in the setting of a myocardial infarction, is associated with substantially increased mortality. (Ref. ACLS, p. 21; Caroline, p. 291)

390. True. The refractory period is the portion of time after a heartbeat when the myocardial cell cannot propagate or conduct an action potential. This extends from the onset of QRS to the apex of the T wave on an ECG. (Ref. ACLS, p. 47; Caroline, p. 257)

391. False. Again, any myocardial cell has the potential to be a pacemaker. When it does so, as during a bradycardia, it is called an escape pacemaker, and the resultant beat is an escape rhythm. (Ref. ACLS, p. 65; Caroline, p. 257)

392. False. The PR interval extends from the beginning of the P wave to the onset of the QRS complex. As the P wave represents the depolarization of the atrium and the QRS complex represents the onset of depolarization of the ventricles, the PR interval does not extend to repolarization of the ventricles. (Ref. ACLS, p. 49; Caroline, p. 259)

393. False. Although hypotension is the hallmark of the patient in cardiogenic shock, hypertension is also found in some patients with a myocardial infarction, particularly those with extreme anxiety. (Ref. ACLS, p. 15; Caroline, p. 266)

394. True. The hallmark of cardiogenic shock, low capillary wedge pressure and cardiac output, is due to loss of the pump's driving ability. (Ref. ACLS, p. 15; Caroline, p. 271)

395. True. The P wave represents atrial depolarization; the PR interval, the delay as the impulses travel from atrium to ventricle; and the QRS, ventricular depolarization. (Ref. ACLS, p. 49)

396. Sinus rhythm at a rate of more than 100 with a fixed 1 : 1 relationship of P to QRS. To be a sinus rhythm, there must be a 1 : 1 relationship between P and QRS complexes. To be a tachycardia, the rate must be greater than 100 in an adult. (Ref. ACLS, p. 57)

397. Sinus rhythm of less than 60, with a fixed 1 : 1 relationship of P to QRS. Sinus bradycardia is most often seen in the functional well-developed athlete with a heart rate of 40. This patient needs to be recognized, but not treated. (Ref. ACLS, p. 51)

8 Central Nervous System

398. Which symptom(s) is present if the tenth cranial nerve has been stimulated?
    A. Bradycardia
    B. Increase in gastric acid secretion
    C. Decrease in AV conduction
    D. All of the above
    E. None of the above

399. A patient with a spinal cord lesion at the level of T-4 should
    A. have no sensation around and below the umbilicus
    B. have no sensation below the nipple line
    C. not be able to move the upper extremities
    D. be able to extend but not flex the elbow
    E. not have sensation below the shoulders

400. In which position should an unconscious patient without a neck injury be transported?
    A. Supine, without a pillow
    B. Trendelenburg
    C. Left lateral and semiprone
    D. Semisitting
    E. Any position

401. Indications of a basal fracture of the skull include
   A. mastoid hematoma
   B. Battle's sign
   C. raccoon eyes
   D. all of the above
   E. B and C

402. What is the postictal state?
   A. State of incontinence
   B. Drowsy feeling after a seizure
   C. Hands-up position of spinal cord trauma
   D. Aura after a seizure
   E. All of the above

403. When trying to determine if a cerebral concussion is the cause of a patient's problem, which is most helpful?
   A. Time
   B. Pupillary changes
   C. Evidence of intracranial pressure
   D. X-ray exam in the ER
   E. Bilateral Babinski signs

404. Which condition or sign has the worst prognosis?
   A. Battle's sign
   B. Epidural hematoma
   C. Cerebral concussion
   D. Penetrating head injury
   E. Subdural hematoma

405. A patient with a basilar skull fracture will have
   1. frontal scalp hematoma
   2. raccoon eyes
   3. Battle's sign
   4. subconjunctival hemorrhage
   A. 1, 2, and 4
   B. 2 and 3
   C. 2, 3, and 4
   D. 4 only
   E. all of the above

406. "Orientation" refers to
   A. a normal neurologic examination
   B. the patient's ability to answer three basic questions
   C. the patient's ability to respond to verbal commands
   D. the level of consciousness
   E. the patient's ability to respond to pain

407. In dealing with an epileptic patient, which emergency procedure should be initiated first?
   A. The patient should be intubated.
   B. The patient should be forcibly restrained until the seizure.
   C. A bite block should be inserted during the contracting stage of the convulsion.
   D. The patient should be protected from injury until the seizure ends.
   E. Phenytoin 100 mg should be injected intravenously.

408. A patient with CSF leaking from the ear should be treated for
   A. skull fracture
   B. tear of the pia mater
   C. basal skull fracture with a dural tear
   D. dural and pia tear
   E. skull fracture with a dural and arachnoid tear

409. If respiratory or cardiovascular function changes after a brain injury, you should suspect a dysfunction in the
   A. brainstem
   B. cerebrum
   C. cerebellum
   D. frontal lobe
   E. all of the above

410. Which compound is necessary for proper functioning of the neurons?
   A. Glucose
   B. Oxygen
   C. Fats
   D. Proteins
   E. A and B

411. Which functions are observed when determining the Glasgow scale?
1. Eye opening
2. Verbal response
3. Response to painful stimuli
4. Memory of the accident
   A. 1, 2, and 3
   B. 1 and 3
   C. 2 and 4
   D. 4 only
   E. All of the above

412. Spinal cord injury is most often seen in association with
   A. pelvic injury
   B. extremity fractures
   C. head injury
   D. chest injury
   E. abdominal injury

413. After a closed-head injury, an adult becomes hypotensive. What is the least likely cause of this hypotension?
   A. Respiratory insufficiency
   B. Associated chest injuries
   C. Spinal cord injury
   D. Associated abdominal injuries
   E. The head injury

414. Why would a comatose patient regain consciousness after administration of naloxone?
   A. It is a brainstem stimulant.
   B. The coma may have been narcotic induced.
   C. It is a cerebral stimulant.
   D. It reverses the effects of drugs that cause comas.
   E. It stimulates the sympathetic nervous system.

415. The shock that follows spinal cord injury is due to
   A. loss of peripheral resistance
   B. hypovolemia resulting from fluid loss
   C. pump failure
   D. the related head injury
   E. respiratory depression

416. Which finding would you see on a patient with a spinal cord lesion at C1−2?
    A. Apnea
    B. Priapism
    C. Paralysis
    D. Areflexia
    E. All of the above

417. Your first action in treating an unconscious patient found slumped over the steering wheel in a van that is on fire because of a gasoline spill is to
    A. apply a cervical collar, then drag the patient out
    B. drag the patient out immediately and run with him or her to safety
    C. apply a backboard and extricate
    D. apply a backboard and collar and then extricate
    E. test for pain response

418. What is an "aura"?
    A. Increased muscle tone
    B. The period after a seizure
    C. Violent contraction of muscles
    D. A time of abnormal perception prior to a seizure
    E. None of the above

419. What important aspects of a seizure should be noted?
    A. Any signs of trauma
    B. Duration of the seizure
    C. Localizing signs
    D. Occurrence of incontinence
    E. All of the above

420. "Status epilepticus" can be defined as
    A. seizures associated with abnormal behavior
    B. repetitive seizures without periods of awakening
    C. a fake seizure
    D. a seizure involving only one side of the body
    E. all of the above

421. Why is glucose 50% administered when seizures are treated in the field?
    A. Hypoglycemia may be the reason for the seizure
    B. The violent contractions of the seizure will lead to hypoglycemia
    C. Hypoglycemia is present in all seizures
    D. The liver's glucose is used up during the seizure
    E. All of the above

422. The organ that controls consciousness and mental processes is the
    A. Spinal cord
    B. Heart
    C. Hypothalamus
    D. Brain
    E. Pituitary

423. The center for reflex action is located in the
    A. medulla
    B. spinal cord
    C. cerebrum
    D. A and C
    E. all of the above

424. The division of the autonomic nervous system that mobilizes energy for emergency situations is the
    A. Parasympathetic system
    B. Sympathetic system
    C. Epinephrine-producing system
    D. Peripheral nervous system
    E. Voluntary nervous system

425. The subsystem of the autonomic nervous system that slows the heart rate and constricts the pupils is the
    A. asympathetic system
    B. visceral afferent system
    C. sympathetic system
    D. parasympathetic system
    E. voluntary afferent system

426. Stimulation of the sympathetic nervous system causes the pupil to
   A. constrict
   B. first dilate, then constrict
   C. dilate
   D. remain normal size
   E. diaphorese

427. Stimulation of the parasympathetic nervous system results in
   1. decreased cardiac strength
   2. increased heart rate
   3. decreased heart rate
   4. decreased electrical excitability
   5. increased electrical excitability
   6. accelerated body functions
      A. 1, 3, and 4
      B. 2, 5, and 6
      C. 1, 3, 4, and 6
      D. 2, 4, and 6
      E. All of the above

428. Which statement(s) is true of acetylcholine (ACh)?
   1. It is present in the parasympathetic branches of the autonomic nervous system only.
   2. It is dependent in action on the presence of α and β receptors.
   3. It is present solely in the sympathetic branch of the autonomic nervous system.
   4. It is present in both sympathetic and parasympathetic ganglia.
      A. 1 only
      B. 4 only
      C. 2 and 4
      D. 1 and 2
      E. 2 and 3

429. The meninges cover the brain and spinal cord. Indicate the correct order from innermost to outermost.
A. Dura mater, pia mater, arachnoid
B. Pia mater, arachnoid, dura mater
C. Arachnoid, pia mater, dura mater
D. Antimater, arachnoid, pia mater
E. Pia mater, antimater, arachnoid

430. The portion of the nervous system that controls involuntary functions of the body is the
A. central nervous system
B. peripheral nervous system
C. autonomic nervous system
D. sympathetic nervous system
E. limbic system

431. Which condition has the worst prognosis?
A. Battle's sign
B. Epidural hematoma
C. Raccoon's eyes
D. Seizure caused by hypoglycemia
E. Overdose of heroin

432. An unconscious patient could be suffering from
A. hypoxia
B. cervical spine injury
C. hypoglycemia
D. head injury
E. all of the above

433. What is the most UNLIKELY finding in a patient who is unresponsive because of an overdose of a depressant drug?
A. Pupillary constriction
B. Hemiparesis, hyperreflexia on the right
C. Pupillary dilation
D. Airway obstruction
E. Snoring respirations

434. Before testing an unconscious head-injured patient's response to pain, you should first
   A. examine the abdomen
   B. test the lower extremity reflexes
   C. protect the neck
   D. test for handgrip
   E. test for Babinski signs

435. What is priapism?
   A. A sustained erection of the penis
   B. Clear discharge from the nose
   C. A variant of angina
   D. A sexual phobia
   E. Difficult intercourse

436. A patient who has a clear discharge from her nose after suffering a possible head injury should be treated for
   A. pulmonary edema
   B. skull fracture with CSF leakage
   C. epistaxis
   D. direct nasal trauma
   E. rhinorrhea

437. In which position should you place a nontrauma comatose patient during transport to the hospital? Assume that the patient is not intubated.
   A. Elevate the legs at a 45° angle
   B. Left lateral, semirecumbent
   C. Trendelenburg
   D. Supine positioning at 10°
   E. None of the above

QUESTIONS 438 and 439: For each numbered item, select the most closely related lettered item. (Letters may be used more than once.)

438. Match the signs with the correct condition.
1. _____ Cerebral edema
2. _____ Injury to lumbar spine
3. _____ Narcotic overdose
4. _____ Stroke
5. _____ Pneumothorax
6. _____ Cardiac pulmonary edema
7. _____ Peritonitis

A. Dysconjugate gaze, facial weakness, paralysis of left side, garbled speech
B. Labored breathing, distended jugular veins, gallop rhythm, rales, rapid pulse
C. Pinpoint pupils; slow, shallow breathing; coma
D. Paralysis and absence of sensation in both legs, normal sensation in arms
E. Patient lying very still, rigid abdomen, absent bowel sounds, rapid pulse
F. Extensor posturing, coma, unequal pupils, periodic respirations
G. Tracheal deviation, respiratory distress, unequal breath sounds, subcutaneous emphysema

439. Match each phrase with the correct portion of the nervous system.
1. _____ Medulla
2. _____ Taste buds
3. _____ Vagus nerve
4. _____ Spinal cord
5. _____ Brain
6. _____ Motor nerves to skeletal muscles

A. Peripheral nervous system
B. Central nervous system
C. Autonomic nervous system

Explanatory Answers

398. D. Tenth (or vagal) nerve stimulation produces all of the symptoms listed. (Ref. Caroline, pp. 111–112)

399. B. The nipple line is located about the T-4 level, the umbilicus about the T-10 level, and the clavicles about the C-3 level for sensation. (Ref. Caroline, p. 357)

400. C. This position allows protection from aspiration. It is often called the "coma" position. (Ref. Caroline, p. 365)

401. D. All indicate a basilar skull fracture. "Battle's sign" is a hematoma about the mastoid bone and is suspicious for a basilar skull fracture. (Ref. Caroline, p. 352)

402. B. The post(or after)ictal state is the sleepiness that the patient feels after the seizure. (Ref. Caroline, p. 366)

403. A. In all head trauma, the most important aspect of the examination is a change in neurologic findings over time. (Ref. Caroline, p. 350)

404. B. Epidural hematomas are arterial in origin; there is usually rapid depression of the level of consciousness. (Ref. Grant, p. 264)

405. B. Subconjunctival hemorrhage has no connotations. Frontal hematomas are not indicative of basilar skull fracture. (Ref. Caroline, p. 352)

406. B. The three basic questions are "who are you?", "where are you?", and "what is the date?" This establishes "orientation" to person, place, and time. (Ref. Caroline, p. 352)

407. D. Usually, protection of the patient until the seizure has passed is all that is required. It is hazardous to try to insert an oral airway of any type. Phenytoin is appropriate, but starts to act only after 30 to 60 minutes. Usually, it is appropriate to use a faster-acting agent such as diazepam first. (Ref. Caroline, p. 367)

408. C. CSF leakage from the ear, "Battle's sign," raccoon eyes, and blood leakage from the ear are all indicative of a basilar skull fracture. (Ref. Caroline, p. 352)

409. A. Trauma to the medulla or brainstem often causes damage to the respiratory and heartbeat centers contained there. (Ref. Caroline, p. 346)

410. E. Come now, this is an easy one. Without sugar and oxygen, the brain does not work! (Ref. Caroline, pp. 183, 362–363)

411. A. The Glasgow coma scale evaluates motor response, eye opening, and verbal response. From these evaluations, a rough prediction can be made about the patient's course. (Ref. Caroline, p. 353)

412. C. The general rule of thumb is that any injury sufficient to fracture the skull has sufficient force to fracture or dislocate the neck. (Ref. Caroline, p. 351)

413. E. It is difficult to lose enough blood inside of the skull to become hypovolemic and hypotensive. (Ref. Caroline, p. 351)

414. B. It is a sad commentary that some members of our society prefer to spend time in drug-induced states rather than reality. Unfortunately, overdose of narcotic preparations is so common in some urban areas that it is wise to consider narcotics as a possible cause of coma in all unconscious patients. Equally unfortunately, some of the newer narcotics do not cause typical pupil constriction signs. (Ref. Caroline, p. 364)

415. A. Although rather rare, spinal or neurogenic shock is caused by loss of vasomotor tone. The wise paramedic should look well for other associated injuries and causes of shock. (Ref. Caroline, p. 356)

416. E. A spinal cord lesion at C1–2 may cause paralysis of all muscles, including those of respiration. A reflex response to this may be priapism. (Ref. Caroline, p. 357)

417. B. This is a life-threatening situation for both patient and rescuer. Dead heroes cannot save lives. (Ref. Caroline, p. 582)

418. D. An aura is the "feeling" that an epileptic has prior to a seizure. It may be an abnormal color perception, a funny smell, or a rushing sound. It is usually the same for every seizure experienced by the epileptic but differs from person to person. (Ref. Caroline, p. 366)

419. E. All of these items convey important information in the diagnosis of seizures. (Ref. Caroline, p. 366)

420. B. Status epilepticus is the occurrence of two or more seizures without awakening between the two seizures. It is a serious disease process with a high mortality. The most common cause of status epilepticus is failure to take prescribed antiseizure medications. (Ref. Caroline, pp. 367, 635)

421. A. Hypoglycemia is an easily treatable cause of seizures and can cause severe brain damage if untreated. (Ref. Caroline, pp. 365–366)

422. D. Obviously, the organ that is the seat of all life is the brain. "I think, therefore I am." (Ref. Caroline, p. 28)

423. B. The major function of the spinal cord is conduction of messages from the brain to the body. (Ref. Caroline, p. 29)

424. B. The "fight-or-flight" phenomenon mobilizes energy for emergency situations and is controlled by the sympathetic nervous system. (Ref. Caroline, p. 30)

425. D. Parasympathetic stimulation decreases rate and strength of cardiac contraction, constricts coronary vessels, causes contraction of the sphincter muscles which results in constriction of the iris of the eye. (Ref. Caroline, pp. 30, 111)

426. C. Sympathetic stimulation causes relaxation of constrictor muscles resulting in dilation of the pupil. This component of the "fight-or-flight" response enables a person to widen their vision. (Ref. Caroline, p. 111)

427. A. The parasympathetic system facilitates digestion of food, slows the heart rate, and makes the heart less excitable. (Ref. Caroline, p. 111)

428. B. Cholinergic fibers release acetylcholine. The cholinergic fibers include (1) all sympathetic and parasympathetic preganglionic axons, (2) all parasympathetic postganglionic axons, and (3) some sympathetic postganglionic axons. The cholinergic sympathetic postganglionic axons include sweat glands, blood vessels in the skin, skeletal muscle, and external genitalia. (Ref. Caroline, pp. 111–112)

429. B. Remembering your basic anatomy, the dura mater (or "tough mother"—loosely translated from the Latin!) is the outermost layer, followed by the arachnoid or spider web–like middle layer. The pia mater is the innermost layer. (Ref. Caroline, p. 28)

430. C. The portion of the nervous system that regulates the activities of smooth muscle, cardiac muscle, and glands is the autonomic nervous system. (Ref. Caroline, p. 30)

431. B. Epidural hematomas are arterial in origin and are usually followed by rapid depression of the level of consciousness and frequently death, if untreated. Both Battle's sign and raccoon's eyes indicate only that the patient has a possible basilar skull fracture. Although the patient with a heroin overdose may die, and may contract AIDS from the needle, ideally this problem is reversible, even in the field. Likewise, hypoglycemia is rapidly treatable. (Ref. Caroline, pp. 352, 362)

432. E. Any of the injuries listed can be found in the patient who has a head injury and is unable to relate past medical illness or injuries to you. (Ref. Caroline, pp. 347–357)

433. B. It would be very unlikely that an overdose would result in signs that mimic a stroke or cord trauma. All of the other findings can be observed in the patient who is unable to maintain a patent airway or is hypoxic from CNS depression. (Ref. Caroline, p. 364)

434. C. Any unconscious patient with a head injury should be presumed to have a cervical spine injury until proven otherwise. (Ref. Caroline, p. 356)

435. E. Priapism is the sustained erection of the penis that is seen with spinal trauma and overdoses of stimulants such as cocaine. These patients have a serious disease and should not be treated in a jocular manner. (Ref. Caroline, p. 357)

436. B. Although the technical name for the clear discharge is rhinorrhea, the patient should be considered to have a basilar skull fracture with a CSF leak through the cribriform plate behind the nose. This fracture may predispose the patient to meningitis, and requires evaluation and treatment. (Ref. Grant, p. 264; Caroline, p. 46)

437. B. The left lateral, semirecumbent position is used for nonintubated patients in a coma not induced by trauma. (Ref. Caroline, p. 365)

438. 1 — F, 2 — D, 3 — C, 4 — A, 5 — G, 6 — B, 7 — E.

439. 1 — B, 2 — A, 3 — C, 4 — B, 5 — B, 6 — A.

9 Soft Tissue Injuries

---

440. Why is bleeding from the large veins in the neck serious?
   A. Air may enter the vein and travel to the heart.
   B. The trachea is close to the veins.
   C. Carbon dioxide cannot be removed from the brain.
   D. Intracranial pressure rises because of the bleeding.
   E. It is impossible to control the flow from these veins except by surgery.

441. An open wound to the anterior neck should be sealed to prevent which life-threatening complication?
   A. Subcutaneous emphysema
   B. Paraplegia
   C. Thyroid damage
   D. Air embolism
   E. Thrombotic embolic phenomenon

442. To which artery would you apply finger pressure to control severe bleeding from the forearm?
   A. Temporal
   B. Radial
   C. Femoral
   D. Brachial
   E. Popliteal

167

443. What type of wound is characterized by jagged skin edges and free bleeding?
    A. Laceration
    B. Incision
    C. Avulsion
    D. Amputation
    E. Excision

444. In the treatment of a patient with an impaled object in the eye, you would do which of the following?
    1. Cover the injured eye with a moist dressing and protective cone.
    2. Check for lacerations by gently pressing on the eyeball.
    3. Remove the foreign body.
    4. Cover the uninjured eye.
        A. 1
        B. 3 and 4
        C. 1 and 4
        D. 1 and 2
        E. All of the above

445. To control bleeding from the anterior nose, you should
    A. use an ice pack on the back of the neck
    B. pinch the nostrils together for at least 10 minutes
    C. tell the patient to sit upright with his head tilted backward
    D. tell the patient to lean forward with his head between his knees
    E. apply ice to the bridge of the nose or forehead

446. You should suspect that a female patient is bleeding internally if
    A. she has a stiff, boardlike abdomen
    B. she is vomiting "coffee ground"–like material
    C. she appears shocky
    D. she has an episode of unexplained syncope
    E. all of the above

447. Which statements are true of electrical burns?
1. The power company should be called immediately if there are fallen wires or other electrical hazards.
2. Respiratory and cardiac arrest are the major problems of victims with electrical burns.
3. Electrical burns can be more serious than they appear.
4. Often there are entry and exit burns where the electricity enters and exits the body.
   A. 2 and 4
   B. 1, 2, and 3
   C. 1 and 4
   D. 1, 2 and 4
   E. All of the above

448. A 23-year-old woman is stabbed by her boyfriend, and a portion of the intestine is protruding through the wound. You should
   A. keep the intestine clean, warm, and dry with a sterile dressing and transport
   B. carefully push the intestine back into the abdomen, cover the wound with a sterile dressing, and transport
   C. cover the wound with a moist, sterile dressing and transport
   D. wash the intestine with sterile water, cover the wound, and transport
   E. wash the intestine with an antiseptic solution, such as povidone–iodine solution, cover the wound with a sterile dressing, and transport

449. There has been a fight at the local bar. One of the victims has been stabbed in the upper chest with an ice pick. As you begin to treat this person, he complains of pain but experiences no dyspnea. The ice pick is protruding from the chest. You should
   A. use a bulk dressing to immobilize the ice pick
   B. after removing the ice pick, use a bulk dressing to control the bleeding
   C. begin mouth-to-mouth respiration and transport immediately
   D. after removing the ice pick, place an airtight dressing over the wound
   E. insert a chest decompression needle in the second intercostal space, at the midclavicular line

450. Why does the application of pressure to a pressure point aid in the control of hemorrhage?
   A. Blood pressure decreases because of dilation of the arteries and veins.
   B. Plasma production increases, which helps coagulation.
   C. Blood flow to the injured site decreases.
   D. Blood clots in the artery at the pressure point.
   E. Anticlotting lymph fluid factors are expressed from the wound.

451. What is the first step taken to control bleeding from a laceration of the forehead?
   A. With an ace bandage, a dressing should be secured over the injured site.
   B. Pressure should be applied to the carotid pressure point.
   C. With a gauze bandage, direct pressure should be applied gently.
   D. Because of the possibility of a skull fracture, bleeding should not be controlled.
   E. Ice should be applied to the back of the neck.

452. If a tourniquet is used to control bleeding, you should do which of the following?
    1. Tighten the tourniquet just enough to stop the flow of blood to the wound.
    2. Use thin wire or string.
    3. Place the tourniquet as close to the wound as possible.
    4. Tag the patient with a note that indicates when the tourniquet was applied.
    A. 1, 2, and 3
    B. 1, 2, and 4
    C. 1, 3, and 4
    D. 2 and 4
    E. All of the above

453. While working, a 35-year-old man tripped on some equipment on the ground and fell against a sharp protrusion. Your examination reveals a sucking chest wound. Your course of treatment should include which of the following?
    1. Positioning the patient on his uninjured side and transport
    2. Positioning the patient on his injured side and transport
    3. Using an occlusive dressing to seal the wound
    4. Telling the patient to breathe deeply to increase the chest cavity pressure
    A. 1, 2, and 3
    B. 2, 3, and 4
    C. 2 and 3
    D. 1 and 3
    E. 3 only

454. During a collision in a soccer game, a young man heard a rib crack. Initially, except for some pain, he felt fine and continued to play. By the time the "field team" arrived, he was breathing with difficulty and had a fast, weak pulse and low blood pressure. He appeared shocky. In addition to the fractured rib, you should suspect
    A. traumatic asphyxia
    B. tension pneumothorax
    C. ruptured colon
    D. laceration of the aorta
    E. simple pneumothorax

455. What type of injury occurs when a whole portion of skin with some of the subcutaneous tissue is torn loose and left as a flap?
 A. Avulsion
 B. Evisceration
 C. Laceration
 D. Aneurysm
 E. Abrasion

456. Which statement concerning loss of the vitreous fluid after an eye injury is correct?
 A. The vitreous fluid will be replenished by the body.
 B. The vitreous fluid can be replaced surgically.
 C. As the vitreous fluid cannot be replaced, the eye will be lost.
 D. The eye will change shape to accommodate for the loss of fluid because the body cannot replace it.
 E. Good artificial vitreous fluid replacements now exist.

457. The thin, delicate membrane that covers the sclera and appears "bloodshot" when it is irritated is called the
 A. retina
 B. conjunctiva
 C. cornea
 D. ciliary muscle
 E. iris

Explanatory Answers

440. A. One of the more common causes of a gas embolus is an opening into the neck or subclavian veins. Particularly when the patient is erect or sitting up, the venous pressure may be less than the air pressure, so that any opening allows air to enter the circulatory system. All of the other answers are simply nonsense. The appropriate way to control this bleeding is with an airtight dressing and direct pressure. Saran wrap will do, but the inner sterile surface of a dressing pack is better. (Ref. Caroline, p. 397)

441. D. The second most lethal complication of open wounds to the neck is an air embolism. (The first, of course, is exsanguination.) (Ref. Caroline, p. 397)

442. D. The proper artery is the artery that supplies blood to the area, which is the brachial artery. The radial artery supplies blood to the hand. (Ref. Caroline, p. 399)

443. A. A laceration is produced by a sharp instrument such as a knife or razor. Although an excision is a surgically produced laceration, the proper answer is the laceration. (Ref. Caroline, p. 378)

444. C. Impaled objects in the globe should never be removed in the field. After the object is removed, the vitreous humor will leak out, and it cannot be replaced. Without the vitreous humor, the patient will be blind. (Ref. Caroline, p. 390)

445. B. Control of anterior epistaxis requires pressure to the nasal septum (also called "Kesselbach's plexus"). Application of ice to the area or to the back of the neck accomplishes nothing. Sitting forward allows the blood to drip from the nose, but does nothing to staunch the bleeding. (Ref. Caroline, p. 395)

446. E. Nancy Caroline mentions reasons A, B, and C in her discussion on internal bleeding. She neglects to tell you that any patient with an unexplained syncope may have blood loss as the cause of that syncope. The question should be easy, because if A, B, and C are true, then the only correct answer should be E. (Ref. Caroline, pp. 401–402)

447. E. Nancy Caroline notes that electric burns may be more serious than they appear. When electric current passes through the body, damage occurs from the site of entry to the site of exit. If the cardiac or respiratory conduction systems are within that pathway, they will be damaged, causing respiratory or cardiac arrest. Because electric current passes through the tissues, the tissues may be destroyed directly, may be damaged by clothing set on fire by the electric current, or may be destroyed by the arc current. Dr. Caroline feels that wooden poles, ropes, and rubber gloves are appropriate to manage the "hot" wire. Many of these accidents occur at night or in rainstorms (or both), and it would be foolhardy to attempt to seek a "nonconductive" puddle. Unless the paramedic has been thoroughly trained in the management of downed high-voltage power lines and has equipment that is rated for the conditions and has been currently inspected, it is far safer to have the electric company turn off the power. I realize that some fire department paramedic rescue squads do, indeed, have both training and equipment to handle this emergency. Most paramedics do not. (Ref. Caroline, pp. 386–387)

448. C. Penetrating intestinal wounds require careful cleansing before the intestines are returned to the abdomen. This cleansing is best done in an operating room rather than at the site of the stabbing. The intestines should NOT be returned to the abdomen before they are cleansed. Answer E is appropriate within the operating room, but is not appropriate for the field. (Ref. Caroline, p. 398)

449. A. As this person has no dyspnea, it is unlikely that he has a tension pneumothorax. In this case, the foreign body should be left in place and the patient should be transported to an emergency department. (Ref. Caroline, pp. 398, 203–204)

450. C. This answer should be obvious. Blood flow to the injured site is decreased. We certainly hope that the blood does not clot in the artery at the site of the pressure. (Ref. Caroline, p. 399)

451. C. The first technique used to control extensive bleeding should always be direct pressure. If there is obvious evidence of a fracture of the skull, then another method should be considered. (Ref. Caroline, p. 399)

452. C. A tourniquet should be considered as a last-resort method of controlling bleeding from an extremity. The usual situation for use is in the patient with an amputation or partial amputation. Tourniquets should always be made of wide material and tightened sufficiently to stop the flow of blood. (Ref. Caroline, p. 401)

453. C. A sucking chest wound should be sealed with an occlusive dressing. After the sucking chest wound is sealed, the patient should be transported as a simple pneumothorax, ie, in a position of comfort. If the patient develops signs of respiratory distress, presume that a tension pneumothorax has developed and release the seal. If this does not help, consider a contralateral chest injury or a hemothorax. (Ref. Caroline, p. 206)

454. B. There is not enough potential for trauma to suspect highly traumatic asphyxia, ruptured colon, or a laceration of the aorta. It is also unlikely that a simple pneumothorax would cause a falling blood pressure and shocky aspect. Suspect a tension pneumothorax but LOOK FOR OCCULT BLEEDING! (Ref. Caroline, p. 205)

455. A. The flap of skin is characteristic of an avulsion. (Ref. Caroline, p. 380)

456. C. The consequences of loss of the vitreous humor from the posterior chamber of the eye are disastrous. Simply, there is no replacement, and the eye is lost. (Ref. AAOS, p. 248)

457. B. This thin membrane is the area most often injured by foreign bodies in the eye, and the site of most infections of the eye. (Ref. AAOS, p. 244)

10 Musculoskeletal Injuries

QUESTIONS 458–475: Select the ONE most appropriate answer.

458. When splinting extremities, you should
   A. leave the fingers or toes exposed whenever possible
   B. bandage the fingers and toes only when the weather is cold
   C. cover the fingers and toes loosely with the bandage
   D. cover the fingers and toes tightly with the bandage
   E. ignore the circulation to the fingers or toes, as the splint will be removed shortly in the emergency department

459. What is the most common complication of an open fracture?
   A. Nerve damage
   B. Unsightly scar
   C. Possible infection
   D. Severe bleeding
   E. Malunion of the bony fragments

460. In the field, which sign of a fracture should not be sought?
   A. Loss of function
   B. Swelling
   C. Ecchymosis
   D. Crepitus
   E. Loss of pulses

461. Which statement is true of a dislocation?
   A. It should be splinted as found.
   B. It is easy to tell the difference between a fracture and a dislocation.
   C. It cannot be splinted.
   D. After gentle manipulation, it should be splinted.
   E. It is never reduced in the field.

462. A sprain is
   A. always less serious than a fracture
   B. easy to distinguish from a fracture in the field
   C. best treated as a fracture in the field
   D. usually not splinted, but the patient should not walk on it
   E. reduced in the field

463. For what is it most appropriate to use pillow splints?
   A. Ankle fracture
   B. Knee fracture
   C. Fracture of the femur
   D. Humerus fracture
   E. Splinting of suspected cervical fracture

464. To treat open (compound) fractures, you should
   A. straighten the afflicted limb and then bandage
   B. use only air (pneumatic) splints for immobilization
   C. irrigate the wound with saline and then apply traction
   D. cover the wound with sterile dressings and splint as found
   E. administer antibiotics intravenously as directed

465. A fractured clavicle can best be immobilized by
   A. using a sling and swathe
   B. applying a rigid splint to the upper arm
   C. air splinting the arm
   D. applying a traction splint
   E. applying a Velpeaux (clavicle straps) dressing

466. In what type of fracture is the break straight across the shaft
of the bone?
   A. Comminuted
   B. Impacted
   C. Transverse
   D. Oblique
   E. Impacted

467. When the ligaments are torn from a forced motion beyond
the normal range of the joint, you have a
   A. sprain
   B. strain
   C. fracture
   D. dislocation
   E. avulsion

468. Muscles that are stretched and sometimes torn because of
overexertion are
   A. fractured
   B. strained
   C. dislocated
   D. sprained
   E. avulsed

469. Complications of pelvic fractures include
   A. urethral injuries
   B. hypovolemic shock
   C. bladder injuries
   D. colon injuries
   E. all of the above

470. What is the best method of immobilizing a fractured femur?
   A. Inflatable splint
   B. Full backboard
   C. Traction splint
   D. Well-padded board splint
   E. Stokes' litter

471. No attempt should be made to straighten any deformity in the
1. femur
2. wrist
3. elbow
4. knee
   A. All of the above
   B. 2, 3, and 4
   C. 2 and 4
   D. 1, 2, and 3
   E. 3 only

472. In falling from her skateboard, a young woman fractures her elbow. You note a normal radial pulse and normal sensation in the fingers before splinting the elbow in a flexed position. After applying the splint, you check the pulse and sensations again. Now the pulse feels weak and your patient is complaining of numbness and tingling in her fingers. You should
   A. transport the patient to a hospital, as nothing can be done in the field
   B. loosen the bandages securing the splint and recheck the pulse and sensation
   C. remove the splint and bandage, reposition the arm, and then resplint with the same splint
   D. remove the splint and bandage, reposition the arm, and then resplint with an air splint
   E. contact base for further instructions

473. The strong, fibrous cords of tissue that attach the muscles to the bones and are important for movement are called
   A. ligaments
   B. cartilage
   C. fibrils
   D. tendons
   E. collaterals

474. With two people working together, what is the appropriate method for immobilizing and transporting a patient with a possible lower spinal injury?
   A. After applying a cervical collar, immobilize the patient in a chair, and then use a chair-lift carry.
   B. Use a short spine board to immobilize the patient, and then use the extremity carry.
   C. Immobilize the patient on a long spine board.
   D. A two-lift and carry provides adequate support for transport of this patient.
   E. Use a breakaway orthopedic litter to expedite application of the device.

475. With a suspected fracture, you should check for
   A. neurologic function distally
   B. crepitus
   C. vascular function distally
   D. A and C
   E. all of the above

Explanatory Answers

458. A. To check the circulation after applying the splint, the fingers and toes need to be exposed. You really do need to check the circulation in all patients. (Ref. Caroline, p. 413)

459. C. Although all of these complications are seen with open fractures, the most common complication is infection resulting from the protruding bone ends. Most patients with open fractures require debridement of the fracture in an operating room before reduction of the fracture. (Ref. Caroline, p. 408)

460. D. Do not make the bone ends grate. If the patient reports it, note it, but do not elicit it. (Ref. Caroline, p. 408)

461. A. The only exception might be when no pulse is present. Caroline notes this possibility with knee dislocations and other authors advocate gentle reduction with no pulses in other extremities. This is NOT a universally accepted protocol, however. Contact base for further orders. (Ref. Caroline, p. 411; Abbott, p. 193)

462. C. Without an X-ray, it is hard to tell the difference between a fracture and a sprain. It is always appropriate to treat the isolated limb injury as a fracture. In multiple trauma, the only splint needed is a properly applied LONG backboard. (Ref. Caroline, p. 411; Abbott, p. 189)

463. A. The pillow splint provides adequate immobilization for the NONambulatory patient's foot and ankle. It is not useful or appropriate for most other fractures. (Ref. Caroline, p. 418)

464. D. If the bone ends withdraw into the wound, they may bring bacteria into the wound, which increases the chance of infection. Traction splints or straightening the wound by hand will make the bone withdraw into the wound. Air splints may be punctured by the bone ends. Antibiotics are appropriate, but are not authorized for the vast majority of EMS units, and hence are not a viable answer. (Ref. Caroline, p. 408)

465. A. Clavicle fractures may be divided into three types: middle, medial, and lateral. The middle is the most common type. Although the vast majority of fractured clavicles are ultimately treated with clavicle straps, you need to ensure that the patient does not have either a medial clavicle fracture or a lateral clavicle fracture by X-ray. Clavicle straps are NOT indicated for either of these two fractures. As adequate immobilization is achieved by the sling and swathe, this is the appropriate care for all three types of fractured clavicles. (Ref. Caroline, p. 418)

466. C. A transverse fracture is always "straight" across the shaft of the bone. (Ref. Caroline, p. 409)

467. A. The sprain is a torn ligament, the strain is a torn muscle. Avulsions of ligaments may occur, and are found in quite severe sprains. (Ref. Caroline, p. 411)

468. B. See comment for Question 467. It should be clearly noted that it is often impossible to differentiate a sprain from a strain or from a fracture in the field. As far as the paramedic is concerned, these injuries should be considered the same while the patient is in the field. This means that the area should be properly immobilized. (Ref. Caroline, p. 411)

469. E. All of these injuries can be noted with a pelvic fracture, including injuries to the rectum, bladder, and urethra. With the massive blood losses sometimes noted in trauma, and the requirement for blood seen in the pelvic fracture, these injuries should never be underestimated. (Ref. AAOS, pp. 206, 288)

470. C. A fractured femur should be immobilized with traction only if there are no other significant injuries. It takes a substantial amount of time for the two-person crew to apply a traction splint. This time may be better spent in overall immobilization with a spine board or in starting large-bore intravenous lines. In the multiple-trauma patient, a backboard is all the splint that is needed, and a "pretty package" is neither needed nor useful. (Ref. AAOS, p. 209)

471. B. These are highly vascular areas with many nerves running near the bones. Manipulation of these areas can cause severe nerve and vascular damage. (Ref. Caroline, p. 412)

472. B. Needless to say, if the bandage is loosened and the pulse returns, you need do nothing further. (Contacting base if the pulse does not come back would then be an excellent idea.) (Ref. Caroline, p. 413)

473. D. Ligaments attach bones to each other. Tendons attach muscle to bone. Fibrils are part of the muscle. Cartilage covers bone. (Ref. Caroline, p. 406)

474. C. Whenever possible, use a long spine board for any potential spinal injuries. The lifts and carries should be used only when it is dangerous or inappropriate to apply a backboard (such as within a burning building). An orthopedic litter is an alternative, but provides less immobilization, at greater cost than a long spine board. (Ref. Abbott, p. 114; AAOS, p. 239; Caroline, pp. 355–362)

475. D. In any fracture, you need to check for both sensation (neurologic function) and pulses (distal vascular function). (Ref. Caroline, p. 408)

11 Multiple Injuries and Triage

QUESTIONS 476–479: Select the ONE most appropriate answer.

476. The signs and symptoms of a tension pneumothorax include all of the following EXCEPT
    A. muffled heart sounds
    B. tracheal deviation
    C. cyanosis
    D. increasing dyspnea
    E. absence of breath sounds

477. Which is not a symptom of cardiac tamponade?
    A. Distant heart sounds
    B. Ankle edema
    C. Distended neck veins
    D. Increased diastolic BP, decreased systolic BP
    E. Hypotension

478. Which is not a sign of hemopericardium?
    A. Shock
    B. Hypertension
    C. Increased jugular venous pressure (distended neck veins)
    D. Narrowing pulse pressure
    E. Muffled or distant heart sounds

479. You are caring for a patient with chest trauma. While palpating the chest, you feel a fine crackling over its surface. This is a sign of
A. hemothorax
B. subcutaneous emphysema
C. interstitial fluid accumulation
D. fractured ribs
E. subcutaneous collection of blood

Explanatory Answers

476. A. Muffled heart sounds are a sign of cardiac tamponade, not tension pneumothorax. (Ref. ACLS, p. 196; Caroline, p. 205)

477. B. Ankle edema develops slowly and is not considered a sign of cardiac tamponade. (Ref. ACLS, p. 196)

478. B. Cardiac tamponade produces hypotension, not hypertension. (Ref. ACLS, p. 196)

479. B. The fine crackling under the skin, often likened to "Rice Krispies," is air—or subcutaneous emphysema as it is better termed. It is associated with a pneumothorax, and may be seen in the absence of fractured ribs. (Ref. Caroline, p. 161)

12 Medical Emergencies

QUESTIONS 480–509: Select the ONE most appropriate answer.

480. You are treating an obese black man who complains of severe headache for the last 14 hours. He also appears weak, feels dizzy, and has blurred vision. His BP is 240/140, pulse is 100 and regular, respirations are 22. During your examination the patient becomes more confused and less responsive. There is no evidence of trauma. This patient is probably experiencing
    A. cardiac tamponade
    B. an acute myocardial infarction
    C. a hypertensive crisis
    D. congestive heart failure
    E. an epidural hematoma

481. Administration of 50% glucose (D_{50}) would be appropriate for
    A. shock
    B. cardiac arrest
    C. coma of unknown etiology
    D. none of the above
    E. all of the above

482. After being awakened from her sleep because of coughing and shortness of breath, a 65-year-old woman has called for an ambulance. You find the woman sitting on the side of the bed, apprehensive, and breathing with difficulty. She tells you that she is being treated for hypertension and takes digoxin and a diuretic. Her pulse is 122, BP is 192/112, and respirations are 36. Her temperature is normal. Diffuse rhonchi, wheezes, and rales are heard on auscultation of the chest. Jugular venous distension is noted. You would treat this woman for
   A. pneumothorax
   B. epiglottitis
   C. pneumonia
   D. asthma
   E. congestive heart failure

483. You are attending a 54-year-old man who is complaining of dyspnea. He is a two-pack-per-day smoker who acknowledges he has a smoker's cough. Over the last few days the cough has become more bothersome and the sputum is now yellow-green and streaked with blood. He appears flush, somewhat cyanotic, and in obvious respiratory distress. His vital signs are pulse 112, BP 150/90, respirations 38, and temperature 102°. On auscultation of the chest, rhonchi and rales are heard on the right side. You suspect he has
   A. toxic inhalation exposure
   B. asthma
   C. bacterial pneumonia
   D. congestive heart failure
   E. aspiration pneumonia

484. You are called to treat a 30-year-old woman who is complaining of dizziness and dyspnea. On questioning this patient, you find that she has been feeling more tired than normal lately, but that the dizzy feeling began today. She also complains of numbness in a stocking–glove pattern and about her lips. She notes no past history of significant illnesses. Your examination shows a thin, anxious woman with a regular pulse of 98, BP of 128/84, and deep respirations of 35. The lungs are clear to auscultation, palpation, and percussion. You suspect that she is suffering from

A. asthma
B. hyperventilation syndrome
C. spontaneous pneumothorax
D. cardiac dysrhythmia
E. diabetic ketoacidosis

485. Two weeks after an uncomplicated abdominal operation (hysterectomy), a 56-year-old woman experiences an abrupt onset of shortness of breath with an intense pain that increases with deep breathing. Your examination finds an anxious, tachypneic female with a BP of 102/60, pulse of 124, and respirations of 34. Her chest is clear to auscultation. You suspect

A. an asthma attack
B. an acute MI
C. pulmonary embolus
D. congestive heart failure
E. spontaneous pneumothorax

486. Vomiting should not be induced in the management of an overdose or intoxication if the patient

A. has ingested tricyclic antidepressants
B. is a child, no matter what has been swallowed
C. is comatose and seizing
D. has ingested hydrofluoric acid
E. has a polypharmaceutical overdose

487. Early in the morning, you respond to a call at the home of a 56-year-old truck driver who is complaining of a severe, "tearing" pain in his back and abdomen. He tells you that he has been suffering from back pain for several months, but his doctor has been unable to determine the cause. His vital signs are pulse 120, BP 110/90, and respirations 28. He appears pale and anxious. There is no JVD. The chest and heart sounds are clear. The abdomen is soft, with a moderately tender, pulsating mass palpable. For this patient, you would
  A. not begin an IV with lactated Ringers to keep a vein open
  B. not warn the hospital to have a surgical team standing by
  C. not administer nitrous oxide
  D. apply MAST but not inflate
  E. not give dopamine by titrated IV infusion

488. A 59-year-old man is complaining of lower left quadrant and extreme back pain. His skin is cool and clammy, and the BP is 50/0. He has an altered level of consciousness. On examination, you are most likely to find
  A. dyspnea
  B. fever
  C. pulmonary edema
  D. pulsatile abdominal mass
  E. pedal edema

489. Localized pain in the lower right quadrant usually signifies
  A. perforation of the gall bladder
  B. appendicitis
  C. perforated intestine
  D. bladder infection
  E. pancreatitis

490. Though conscious and somewhat confused, your patient is able to follow commands and has no apparent physical injuries. There is a Medic-Alert tag around her neck that states she is a diabetic. What treatment should be given after completing your initial survey?
  - **A.** The patient should be transported to a hospital for an insulin injection.
  - **B.** D_5W 50–100 cc should be given immediately.
  - **C.** The patient should be given some source of sugar by mouth.
  - **D.** To determine the exact problem, examination of the patient should be continued.
  - **E.** An intravenous infusion of normal saline solution should be started immediately.

491. Which of the following signs or symptoms is NOT found in salicylate intoxication?
  - **A.** Fever
  - **B.** Vomiting
  - **C.** Bradycardia
  - **D.** Coma
  - **E.** Hyperpnea

492. An unresponsive patient with respirations of 38 per minute has a "fruity" odor to her breath. What clue would the paramedic be looking for if the refrigerator was checked?
  - **A.** Drugs
  - **B.** Alcohol
  - **C.** Insulin
  - **D.** Vitamins
  - **E.** Antabuse

493. If a diabetic has not taken her insulin or has overeaten, the deficiency of insulin usually leads to
  - **A.** metabolic acidosis
  - **B.** hypoglycemia
  - **C.** respiratory acidosis
  - **D.** metabolic alkalosis
  - **E.** fructosis

494. If insulin is not available to the body
   A. the glucose level falls below normal because the liver is not stimulated to release the sugar
   B. glucose cannot cross the cell membrane
   C. starches and fats cannot be changed into glucose
   D. the cells will not be able to use oxygen to form usable energy and carbon
   E. carbon dioxide will rapidly build up and cause a profound acidosis

495. Which statements are true of diabetes?
   1. The comatose patient frequently is dehydrated.
   2. Abnormal metabolism is usually the cause of the diabetic ketoacidosis.
   3. There is too much glucose in the blood in hyperglycemia.
   4. Because of the elevated level of acids in the blood, the respirations of a victim of diabetic coma are deep and fast.
   A. 1 and 3
   B. 2, 3, and 4
   C. 1, 2, and 4
   D. 4 only
   E. All of the above

496. If your unconscious patient has a slow pulse, tachypnea, cold, dry skin, and an acetone odor to his breath, an associated finding may be
   A. liver failure
   B. hyperglycemia
   C. respiratory acidosis
   D. high insulin
   E. metabolic alkalosis

497. You find a 24-year-old man writhing on the floor, crying in pain. He complains of a sudden onset of a dull ache on his right side 2 hours ago. This pain has steadily worsened. It is crampy and radiates to his right groin. His vital signs are BP 150/90, pulse 100, and respirations 20. This patient should not
A. inhale nitrous oxide for the pain
B. be given an intravenous infusion
C. be treated with rapid application and inflation of MAST
D. be transported in a position of comfort
E. be monitored for heart rhythm

498. What is a possible diagnosis for the patient described in Question 497?
A. Full bladder
B. Renal stone
C. Aortic aneurysm
D. Acute appendicitis
E. Ruptured spleen

499. Should syrup of ipecac be given immediately after charcoal?
A. Yes, charcoal improves the action of the ipecac.
B. No, ipecac and charcoal react together to form an acid that burns the stomach.
C. Yes, ipecac works only in the presence of charcoal.
D. No, the charcoal is likely to be vomited.

500. Poisoning symptoms include
A. irritation of the skin
B. depression of the circulatory system
C. shortness of breath
D. cyanosis
E. all of the above

501. In children, what is the proper dose of syrup of ipecac for inducing vomiting to eliminate poisons?
  A. 60 cc, followed by several glasses of water
  B. 15 cc, followed by several glasses of water
  C. One glass of water, followed by 15 cc
  D. Several glasses of water, followed by several teaspoons
  E. 15 cc of ipecac, followed by 60 g of charcoal

502. Which poison should not be eliminated by vomiting?
  A. Sleeping pills
  B. Household lye
  C. Aspirin
  D. Poisonous berries
  E. Acetaminophen

503. In treating a patient in anaphylactic shock, you would
  A. place cold compresses on any swelling and give liquids
  B. administer oxygen and wait for the reaction to subside
  C. transport to a medical facility immediately
  D. place the victim in a supine position until the reaction clears
  E. give nitroglycerin by mouth to decrease the hypertensive reaction

504. One of the symptoms of anaphylactic shock is
  A. hypovolemia
  B. hypertension
  C. bronchoconstriction
  D. sepsis
  E. bradycardia

505. You are called to a lakeside picnic where a 21-year-old man has suddenly collapsed. The victim's face and tongue are swollen, and the lips appear cyanotic. Though there are no signs of visible injury, the arms, legs, and face are covered with red, swollen areas. You would treat this patient for
  A. anaphylaxis
  B. hypoglycemia
  C. Jimson weed poisoning
  D. myocardial infarction
  E. mushroom poisoning

506. What is NOT a contraindication to the administration of ipecac?
   A. A 24-year-old para 1 gravida 2 woman who has ingested 100 acetaminophen tablets
   B. A 64-year-old man with acute crushing chest pain following an intentional ingestion of clonidine
   C. A 3-year-old child who is postictal from two consecutive seizures following an ingestion of multiple medications from her grandmother's medicine cabinet
   D. A 35-year-old woman who has ingested strychnine
   E. An 18-year-old man with a possible ingestion of 100 tricyclic antidepressant tablets.

507. A 21-year-old woman has just had a seizure. One of the bystanders notes that the patient "does drugs" frequently. Which of the following would be an UNLIKELY cause of seizures?
   A. Meningitis
   B. Overdose of lidocaine
   C. Hypoglycemia
   D. Diabetic ketoacidosis
   E. Hypoxia

508. Which is NOT a type of seizure activity?
   A. Grand mal seizures
   B. Jacksonian or focal motor seizures
   C. Psychomotor seizures
   D. Cerebellar seizures
   E. Absence seizures

509. What is the most common symptom of elevated blood pressure?
   A. Dizziness
   B. Late-afternoon headache
   C. Epistaxis
   D. Headache upon arising
   E. Unilateral blurry vision

QUESTION 510: For each numbered item, select the most closely related lettered item. (Letters may be used more than once.)

510. In the following predicaments, decide if
   A. vomiting should be induced
   B. vomiting should not be induced
   1. _____ Two elderly ladies just served their middle-aged guest a glass of milk laced with arsenic.
   2. _____ A 47-year-old homosexual man ingested 65 diazepam (Valium) tablets 45 minutes after receiving his blood test confirming HIV infection. He is alert and responsive.
   3. _____ A 14-year-old ingested about 50 mL of gasoline while siphoning some gas out of a "friend's" car. He was brought in by the police in handcuffs.
   4. _____ A 3-year-old girl swallowed 250 mL of drain cleaner she found in a Coke bottle.
   5. _____ A 24-year-old woman who ingested the contents of a bottle of chlorpromazine (Thorazine) is confused and easily lapses into sleep.
   6. _____ Ten minutes prior to your arrival, a 4-year-old ate 40 adult iron tablets while playing with a friend.

Explanatory Answers

480. C. This is a classic case of hypertensive crisis with hypertensive encephalopathy. As there is no history of trauma, an epidural hematoma is unlikely. (Ref. Caroline, p. 275)

481. C. For a patient with coma of unknown origin, either blood sugar must be determined with a rapid method such as Dextrostix or the patient should be given 50 cc of 50% dextrose. The presence of alcohol, trauma, or drugs should not influence this treatment plan, unless the trauma or the overdose was observed. (Ref. Caroline, p. 365)

482. E. This is the picture of a patient in congestive heart failure. Her history of shortness of breath, jugular venous distension, and rales and wheezes should prompt you to look for either pneumonia or congestive failure. Without a temperature, the best bet is congestive heart failure. The digoxin and diuretics in her past history should pretty much clinch the diagnosis. (Ref. Caroline, pp. 269–270)

483. C. This is the classic picture of bacterial pneumonia. His fever, sputum production, auscultory findings, and respiratory rate all point to a bacterial infection. It is possible that the patient has an aspiration pneumonia, but there exist no historical data to support that contention. (Ref. Caroline, p. 208)

484. B. The most common disease listed that fits this picture is hyperventilation syndrome. It would be a bad mistake to assume that this is the cause and just reassure her, however. This clinical picture could also be found in cases of a pulmonary embolus and the patient needs to be evaluated for this. Diabetic ketoacidosis could also have the deep and fast respiratory rate, but there would probably be a fruity odor to the breath (this may not yet be present) and the patient would most likely know about her diabetes at the age of 30. One would expect with deep respirations and no wheezes that this is not asthma and a new onset of asthma at age 30 is not a usual pattern. Likewise, a spontaneous pneumothorax would likely have some component of chest pain, a dysrhythmia, and some irregularity of pulse. (Ref. Caroline, p. 215)

485. C. Although this picture may also fit the signs of a spontaneous pneumothorax, the surgery 2 weeks earlier should tip you off to look for a pulmonary embolus. Asthma, congestive heart failure, and an acute MI are remote possibilities given this presentation. (Ref. Caroline, p. 215, Table 5-3)

486. C. Induction of vomiting is not appropriate when the patient is either comatose or seizing. Although hydrofluoric acid is a strong acid and vomiting usually is not induced in patients who have ingested either strong acids or strong alkalis, the systemic toxicity of fluoride is sufficiently dangerous so that the risk of esophageal or gastric perforation is less than the risk of allowing the agent to remain in the stomach. (Ref. Caroline, p. 441)

487. E. This is the classic presentation of an abdominal aortic aneurysm (AAA). When managing an AAA, one does not suddenly increase the BP with pressor agents. The leaking AAA may rupture. All of the other treatments are appropriate. Nitrous oxide may provide pain relief without masking any abdominal pathology for the emergency physician's and surgeon's evaluation. (Ref. Caroline, p. 459)

488. D. Cool clammy skin precludes fever, so although sepsis may also cause this picture, the only one that fits is aortic abdominal aneurysm. (Ref. Caroline, p. 459)

489. B. All of these have caused right lower quadrant abdominal pain, but acute appendicitis is most often the cause. (Ref. Caroline, p. 457)

490. C. For an alert, awake patient, use the oral route. (Ref. Caroline, p. 423)

491. C. The patient who has ingested salicylates is often vomiting and may be dehydrated. These conditions lead to tachycardia, not bradycardia. (Ref. Caroline, p. 445)

492. C. This is a picture of diabetic ketoacidosis, hence the search for insulin, which must be kept refrigerated. (Ref. Caroline, p. 423)

493. A. Metabolic acidosis is the usual finding in diabetic keto-acidosis. It may be seen in the early stages with an associated respiratory alkalosis as the patient attempts to correct the acid load by breathing more rapidly. (Ref. Caroline, p. 422)

494. B. The body attempts to switch to alternate metabolic path-ways to obtain the energy needed when glucose cannot cross the cell membrane appropriately because of the lack of insulin. Al-though there may be an associated profound acidosis, this is due to pileup of fat metabolism acids, not to carbon dioxide. Blood sugar levels rapidly climb as the fats and starches are processed but not used. (Ref. Caroline, pp. 422–423)

495. E. All of the reasons listed are true. Hyperglycemia is too much glucose, and because of the increase in blood glucose, the patient must urinate more frequently than necessary, hence dehy-dration. The body will try alternate pathways to provide food for the cells and the by-products of this alternate metabolism cause a metabolic acidosis. Respiratory correction of a metabolic acidosis helps by rapidly breathing off carbon dioxide. (Ref. Caroline, pp. 422–423)

496. B. This is a by-the-book description of diabetic ketoacidosis; hence hyperglycemia should be found. (Ref. Caroline, pp. 422–423)

497. C. There are no indications for the use of MAST in this patient with possible renal colic. Relief of pain with either nar-cotics or nitrous oxide is appropriate after consultation with the base physician. As with all patients, transport in the position of comfort unless medical reasons dictate otherwise. This patient's heart rate should be monitored. (Ref. Caroline, p. 459)

498. B. This is a classic description of the pain of renal colic. (Ref. Caroline, p. 460)

499. D. As ipecac is designed to induce vomiting, it makes little sense to give it to the patient and then give any other medication by mouth. (Ref. Caroline, p. 441)

500. E. A poison can produce any of the symptoms noted, and quite a few more. Poisons can gain access to the body by ingestion, inhalation, surface absorption, or injection. (Ref. Caroline, pp. 445–448)

501. B. The appropriate dose of ipecac to induce vomiting in a child is one half of a single dose bottle (30-cc bottle). (Ref. Caroline, p. 445)

502. B. In general, vomiting should not be induced in any patient who has ingested a strong acid or alkali. An exception may be made for hydrofluoric acid ingestions, as the toxicity of the fluoride ion is more severe than the chances of gastric or esophageal rupture if the patient vomits. (Ref. Caroline, p. 446)

503. C. The only logical solution to this question of the answers listed is to transport the patient. While you are transporting the patient, give epinephrine, start an intravenous line, and administer oxygen by mask. Intubation of this patient may be urgently needed and you should be prepared. (Ref. Caroline, p. 425)

504. C. The patient is usually tachycardic and hypotensive, and has severe dyspnea. Wheezing frequently signals the onset of severe and life-threatening bronchoconstriction. Sepsis is not found. (Ref. Caroline, pp. 424–425)

505. A. This patient should be considered to have anaphylaxis because of the sudden onset, the facial swelling, and the collapse. It is unlikely that hypoglycemia or myocardial infarction would present with this picture. Mushroom or Jimson weed poisoning takes much longer and does not produce this picture. (Ref. Caroline, pp. 424–425)

506. C. This is a classic hypertensive crisis with hypertensive encephalopathy. Nausea and vomiting are common and are frequently followed by seizures and coma. This patient needs rapid intervention to lower the blood pressure. (Ref. Caroline, p. 276)

506. E. Ingestion of stimulants (such as strychnine), pregnancy, seizures, and possible acute myocardial infarction are all absolute contraindications for administration of ipecac. Most paramedics know the usual contraindications of coma and corrosives and understand the controversy surrounding the use of ipecac in ingestions of petroleum distallates. Pregnancy and acute myocardial infarction are commonly missed in testing, however. (Ref. Caroline, p. 446)

507. D. Hypoxia, meningitis, and hypoglycemia are common causes of seizures in emergency medicine in general and in users of recreational drugs in particular. Fortunately, an overdose of lidocaine is uncommon but may well cause seizures. (It is sometimes used to "cut" or dilute street drugs.) Diabetic ketoacidosis does not usually cause seizures. (Ref. Caroline, p. 366)

508. E. Absence or petit mal seizures are chiefly found in children. Grand mal or generalized motor seizures are characterized by tonic–clonic motions. An altered personality state may signify a temporal lobe or psychomotor seizure. Scar tissue or tumor in the brain may indicate a focal area of irritation causing a jacksonian or focal motor seizure. (Ref. Caroline, p. 366)

509. E. The most common symptom of hypertension is an occipital headache upon arising. This headache tends to resolve by afternoon. (Ref. Caroline, p. 274)

510. 1—A, 2—A, 3—B, 4—B, 5—B, 6—A. There is a good deal of controversy regarding the use of ipecac in ingestions of petroleum products. Although in the past, teaching was that ipecac should not be used in these cases, recent work has demonstrated its relative safety. Generally, it is not recommended for use in field situations. It should not be used in patients who have ingested caustics or who are not able to protect their airway. (Ref. Caroline, p. 447)

13 Obstetrics

QUESTIONS 511-537: Select the ONE most appropriate answer.

511. During pregnancy, the fetus receives nourishment and eliminates its wastes through the
    A. ovary
    B. placenta
    C. umbilical cord
    D. adnexa
    E. uterus

512. What is an undeliverable position?
    A. Limb presentation
    B. Prolapsed cord
    C. Breech birth
    D. Shoulder dysoctocia
    E. Right occiput anterior

513. What does bulging of the perineum during labor indicate?
    A. The delivery will be complicated, and rapid transport to the hospital is necessary.
    B. The baby will be large and perineal tearing is possible.
    C. The baby's presentation is abnormal, and rapid transport to the hospital is necessary.
    D. Delivery is imminent.
    E. The patient has about a half-hour until the baby is delivered.

514. Which conditions would necessitate emergency transport of a pregnant patient?
   1. Breech presentation
   2. Cephalic presentation
   3. Prolapse of the umbilical cord
   4. Eclampsia with seizures
   A. 2 and 3
   B. 1, 3, and 4
   C. 3 and 4
   D. 4 only
   E. All of the above

515. If you are treating a para 6 pregnant woman who feels she is about to have a bowel movement, you should
   A. reassure the woman, and help her go to the bathroom with a chaperone
   B. reassure the woman, encourage her to use breathing techniques, and transport rapidly with the legs together to prevent immediate delivery
   C. reassure the woman, encourage her to use breathing techniques, and prepare for delivery
   D. reassure the woman, have her rest with legs together, and prepare for catheterization
   E. administer 5 mg of diazepam

516. You respond to a call to help a 21-year-old woman in stage I labor. In answer to your questions, she tells you that she is "taking blood pressure medicine, has had the usual swelling for most of the pregnancy, and her urine is funny." Based on this information, you should
   A. transport with lights and sirens
   B. observe seizure precautions, monitor vital signs, and transport as usual with close supervision
   C. observe seizure precautions, monitor vital signs, and transport with lights and sirens and close supervision
   D. after communicating with medical base, proceed with the normal treatment of a woman in labor
   E. immediately deliver the child and then transport as usual with two patients

517. Marty Jones gave birth to a baby girl at 2:45 PM. The delivery went well, but it is now 3:30 and you are still waiting for the placenta to be delivered. As the assisting paramedic, you decide to
    A. transport the patient as you continue to observe her
    B. transport the patient as you manually attempt to remove the placenta
    C. attempt to deliver the placenta by applying gentle pressure on the cord
    D. insert your hand into the vagina and gently, manually remove the placenta
    E. use Magill forceps to remove the placenta

518. You are treating a 23-year-old woman complaining of abdominal pain. Your examination reveals tenderness and pain in the right lower quadrant and right shoulder discomfort. The BP is 92/60. She tells you that her last menstrual period was about 6 weeks ago. You suspect that this woman is experiencing a(n)
    A. attack of appendicitis
    B. gall bladder spasm
    C. ectopic pregnancy
    D. kidney stone
    E. all of the above

519. The umbilical cord connects the baby within the uterus to the
    A. perineum
    B. amnionic sac
    C. placenta
    D. cervix
    E. vulva

520. In which position is the baby's head during a normal delivery?
    A. Face down
    B. Face up
    C. Face turned to right
    D. Chin first
    E. Buttocks first

521. After the placenta is delivered, you should
  A. place it in a plastic bag and transport it to the hospital with the mother
  B. wrap it securely, then discard it
  C. leave it with the mother
  D. place it on the mother's breast
  E. none of the above

522. What action should be undertaken to reduce serious bleeding that appears immediately after a delivery?
  A. Place ice packs at the vaginal opening.
  B. Rush the woman to the hospital.
  C. Pack the vaginal opening with tampons.
  D. Gently massage the uterus.
  E. Pack the vagina with sterile gauze and towels.

523. If the amniotic sac enclosing the fetus has not ruptured prior to birth, you should
  A. puncture the sac and begin CPR immediately
  B. continue with the delivery as the sac does not present a problem for the infant
  C. puncture the sac and remove it from the fetus
  D. slow the progress of the delivery and transport immediately
  E. immediately cross-clamp the umbilical cord and cut it

524. If the umbilical cord appears to be hemorrhaging at the point where it was cut and tied, you should
  A. tie or clamp the cord again close to the first knot
  B. transport immediately
  C. disregard it because the bleeding will not harm the infant
  D. untie the knot on the cord and replace it with an umbilical clamp
  E. immediately manually extract the placenta

525. When managing a prolapsed umbilical cord, you should
    A. wrap the exposed cord in moist, sterile dressings and transport
    B. slow the delivery by applying even pressure on the baby's head
    C. gently replace the cord in the vagina
    D. allow the delivery to continue, as repositioning of the mother is all that is necessary
    E. manually rupture the amniotic membrane

526. If the woman's abdomen is still distended and her contractions continue after delivery, you should suspect
    A. trauma to the uterus
    B. premature delivery of the placenta
    C. multiple birth
    D. severe postpartum hemorrhage
    E. placenta previa

527. What is the main function of amniotic fluid?
    A. Protects and supports the placenta
    B. Supplies the fetus with oxygen
    C. Protects and supports the fetus
    D. Lubricates the baby during delivery
    E. Provides lubrication during the sexual act

528. You are attending a woman with a breech birth. If the baby's head is not delivered within a certain time, you should
    A. use a clamp to keep the vaginal wall away from the baby's face
    B. pull on the baby's trunk and legs to speed the delivery
    C. insert your gloved hand in the vagina and use fingers to make a airway for the baby
    D. place an "S" tube or other airway in the vagina, close to the baby's face
    E. cut and clamp the umbilical cord

529. If you are called to assist a woman in labor, and the baby's arm or leg is the presenting part, you should
    A. immediately transport this woman to the hospital
    B. push the presenting part back into the vagina
    C. facilitate the delivery by using the presenting part to gently manipulate the baby's body
    D. pull on the presenting part to deliver the baby
    E. cut and clamp the umbilical cord

530. During a breech delivery, you must act to prevent suffocation if the head is not spontaneously delivered within
    A. 10 minutes
    B. 6 minutes
    C. 3 minutes
    D. 2 minutes
    E. 1 minute

531. What is one of the immediate dangers of rapid, uncontrolled delivery of the baby's head?
    A. Fetal asphyxia
    B. Tearing of the perineum
    C. Abruptio placentae
    D. Placenta previa
    E. Apgar's syndrome

532. When caring for a woman who is experiencing third trimester bleeding, you should
    A. thoroughly palpate the abdomen
    B. ensure that delivery is not imminent by performing a pelvic exam
    C. pack the vagina with tampons or sterile gauze
    D. tell the woman to see her doctor in the morning
    E. notify the hospital of the problem, administer oxygen, transport immediately, and start an IV enroute to the hospital

533. Hypovolemic shock in a pregnant woman may be caused by
   A. retained placenta
   B. placenta previa
   C. abruptio placentae
   D. postpartum hemorrhage
   E. all of the above

534. What action should be undertaken if the placenta is not delivered immediately?
   A. To help the placenta separate, vigorously rub the abdomen.
   B. To help the placenta separate, pull on the cord.
   C. Observe the mother while continuing preparations for transport.
   D. To aid delivery of the placenta, gently place your hand in the vagina.
   E. Pack the vagina with sterile gauze.

535. Abruptio placentae, a complication of pregnancy that compromises the life of the mother and the baby, usually occurs
   A. in the third trimester and may or may not involve visible bleeding
   B. in the third trimester and involves visible bleeding
   C. early in the pregnancy and involves visible bleeding
   D. in the first trimester and there is no visible bleeding
   E. in the second trimester and may cause seizures

536. You are called to care for a woman who is 8 months pregnant. She is experiencing a small amount of bright red vaginal bleeding, but she is in no pain. A possible cause of her symptoms is
   A. abruptio placenta
   B. ruptured membranes
   C. placenta previa
   D. spontaneous abortion
   E. toxemic reaction

537. What is an abortion?
   A. A birth defect that allows little chance for survival
   B. Birth of a fetus before it has developed enough to survive
   C. A stillbirth
   D. An operation to remove a fetus
   E. Loss of a pregnancy before 20 weeks of gestation for any reason

---

QUESTION 538: For each numbered item, select the most closely related lettered item. (Letters may be used more than once.)

---

538. Indicate the stage of labor described.
   1. _____ Contractions occur every 8 minutes and last 30 seconds
   2. _____ Placenta is delivered
   3. _____ There is a gush of blood and the umbilical cord seems to lengthen where it protrudes from the vagina
   4. _____ Contractions occur every 2 minutes and last 60 seconds
   5. _____ Birth of the baby to the birth of the placenta
   6. _____ Cervical dilation of 1–4 cm
   7. _____ Crowning
   8. _____ Cervical dilation of 10 cm to birth of the baby
   9. _____ First true contractions to complete cervical dilation

   A. Stage I
   B. Stage II
   C. Stage III

Explanatory Answers

511. B. The placenta serves as the organ of nourishment, respiration, and waste elimination for the fetus. (Ref. Caroline, p. 482)

512. A. A limb presentation is always undeliverable. This patient must be taken to the hospital for a cesearian section. In many cases, a patient with a prolapsed cord will be require a cesearian section, but this presentation does not prevent birth. ROA is of course the most common presentation. (Ref. Caroline, p. 498)

513. D. When the perineum starts to bulge, the delivery is imminent and the baby will soon start to crown. (Ref. Caroline, p. 482)

514. C. Prolapse of the cord is an emergency for the child. Eclampsia with seizures is an emergency for both mother and child. (Ref. Caroline, pp. 487, 498)

515. C. The use of the legs together position to delay birth is more effective if it had been taken about 9 months earlier. It is ineffective in delaying the imminent delivery. The fact that the delivery is imminent should preclude further transportation, particularly for a patient who has had six prior deliveries. (Ref. Caroline, p. 489)

516. B. These are the signs of eclampsia. Although the patient has not had a seizure, flashing lights may provoke such seizures. A calm course is indicated for this patient. (Ref. Caroline, p. 487)

517. A. There is usually little that is emergent about the third stage of delivery. Manual removal of the placenta in the field is not appropriate. Magill forceps are used to insert endotracheal tubes. (Ref. Caroline, p. 494)

518. C. Any female of childbearing age with abdominal pain and menstrual irregularity should be suspected of having an ectopic pregnancy. Although all of the other conditions can cause right-sided abdominal pain, only the ectopic pregnancy is associated with menstrual irregularity. (Ref. Caroline, p. 483)

519. C. The placenta is connected to the baby by the umbilical cord. (Ref. Caroline, p. 482)

520. A. Right occiput anterior (ROA) is the most common presentation. That is, the baby's face is slightly to the left and facing down. (Ref. Grant, p. 392)

521. A. The placenta may offer the physician clues to potential birth defects and should be transported to the hospital. If a plastic bag is available, it should be used; if not, a basin with a towel over it will suffice. (Ref. Caroline, p. 494)

522. D. The first step in decreasing bleeding postpartum should be to gently massage the uterus. At the same time, encourage the infant to nurse at the mother's breast. These two measures often stop even the most severe postpartum hemorrhage. Packing the vagina is absolutely contraindicated in the field. (Ref. Caroline, p. 500)

523. C. One should always do the simplest intervention first to remedy the condition. The amniotic sac will obstruct breathing and should be removed. (Ref. Caroline, p. 490)

524. A. If the knot or clamp is ineffective, do it again. (Ref. Caroline, p. 493)

525. B. The knee–chest position can also be used to relieve the pressure on the cord. (Ref. Caroline, p. 496)

526. C. If the abdomen remains distended, you should strongly suspect another fetus. (Ref. Caroline, p. 498)

527. C. Amniotic fluid acts as a "water cushion" for the fetus. (Ref. Caroline, p. 482)

528. C. When attending a breech birth, the paramedic needs to make an airway through which the baby can breathe. (Ref. Caroline, p. 496)

529. A. An arm or leg presentation is not deliverable, and will require surgical intervention for either a viable child or a living mother. (Ref. Caroline, p. 498)

530. D. Although the fetus is more tolerant of hypoxia than an adult, blood flow to the baby is reduced by the pressure of the head on the umbilical cord. (Ref. Caroline, p. 496)

531. B. The most significant danger of the rapid descent of the baby's head through the birth canal is tearing of the vagina and perineum. (Ref. AAOS, p. 400; Caroline, p. 500)

532. E. Third trimester bleeding is potentially life-threatening for both mother and child. This patient should never have a vaginal exam in the field and the vagina should not be packed. Immediate transport is indicated. (Ref. Caroline, p. 487)

533. D. Any of these may lead to hypovolemia from uncontrolled bleeding. (Ref. Caroline, pp. 486, 494, 500)

534. C. The placenta normally may not deliver for 20–30 minutes. Nothing should be done in the field for this condition, in most cases. After the placenta separates, gentle massage of the uterus may stimulate contractions and hasten delivery of the placenta. (Ref. Caroline, p. 494)

535. B. Abruptio placentae, early separation of the placenta, usually occurs in the last or third trimester and involves hidden bleeding. Eclampsia causes seizures. (Ref. Caroline, p. 498)

536. C. Although a spontaneous abortion can occur at 8 months of pregnancy (32 weeks), it is more properly termed a premature delivery and is accompanied by the usual cramping pains. Likewise, ruptured membranes are accompanied by a gush of fluid, not blood. Abruptio placentae is most likely not to involve bleeding, whereas placenta previa is associated with external bleeding and is the correct answer. Toxemia has nothing to do with bleeding. (Ref. Caroline, p. 498)

537. E. Loss of pregnancy before it is greater than 20 weeks of gestation is termed an abortion. Abortions may be therapeutic or spontaneous. Although D is technically an abortion, it is an incomplete answer. (Ref. Caroline, p. 486)

538. 1—A, 2—C, 3—C, 4—B, 5—C, 6—A, 7—B, 8—B, 9—A. (Ref. Caroline, p. 482)

14 Pediatrics

539. What is the leading cause of death in children over 1 year of age?
   A. Self-inflicted wounds
   B. Meningitis
   C. Congenital anomalies
   D. Trauma accidents
   E. Pneumonia and other infections

540. Which site is preferred for peripheral intravenous lines in children?
   A. Lower extremity
   B. Upper extremity
   C. Neck
   D. Scalp
   E. All of the above

541. How many watt seconds of electrical energy are recommended to defibrillate a pediatric patient?
   A. 200 watt seconds
   B. 6 watt seconds/kg
   C. 4 watt seconds/kg
   D. 2 watt seconds/kg
   E. 1 watt seconds/kg

542. Which sign is often absent in children with poor air exchange due to respiratory disease?
   A. Neck retractions
   B. Nasal flaring
   C. Intercostal retractions
   D. Abdominal breathing
   E. Wheezing

543. Which is NOT an appropriate technique for management of seriously ill or injured children?
   A. Separate them from their parents to avoid potential parental psychic trauma.
   B. Be calm, patient, and gentle.
   C. Be honest and tell them that something will hurt if it is going to be painful.
   D. Comfort children's fears, even when the fears are quite irrational.
   E. Ensure that the child is covered and heat loss is prevented.

544. Which of the following is NOT true of croup?
   A. It is most often a viral illness
   B. It is most often seen between 6 months and 4 years of age.
   C. The child with croup has a high-pitched, barking cough.
   D. Croup is treated by intubation or tracheotomy.
   E. Croup is often worse at night.

545. Which arrhythmias are the most frequent cause of cardiac arrest in infants and children?
   A. Bradyarrhythmias and various degrees of block
   B. Ventricular fibrillation and bradyarryhthmias
   C. Ventricular tachycardia and ventricular fibrillation
   D. Various degrees of block and ventricular fibrillation

546. What is NOT true of bronchiolitis?
  A. Bronchiolitis occurs in the child under 1 year of age.
  B. Bronchiolitis responds well to epinephrine.
  C. A child with bronchiolitis has wheezes in all lung fields.
  D. Bronchiolitis is often caused by a viral or bacterial illness.
  E. The child with bronchiolitis may be more comfortable in the erect or semisitting position.

547. Which of the following signs or symptoms is NOT seen in croup but is often found in acute epiglottitis?
  A. Pain on swallowing
  B. Drooling
  C. Fever
  D. Rib retractions
  E. Expiratory stridor

548. For a child, the recommended dose of atropine is
  A. 1–3 mg/kg, given once
  B. 1–3 mL/kg, repeated in 5 minutes
  C. 0.5–1.0 mg/kg, repeated every 5 minutes to a maximum dose of 5 mg
  D. 0.01–0.03 mg/kg, repeated every 5 minutes to a maximum dose of 1 mg
  E. 0.5 mg/kg, repeated every 5 minutes to a maximum dose of 2 mg

549. Which endotracheal tube is best suited for a 2- to 3-year-old child?
  A. 3.0-mm internal diameter (ID) cuffed tube
  B. 3.5-mm ID uncuffed tube
  C. 4.0-mm ID cuffed tube
  D. 5.0-mm ID cuffed tube
  E. 6.0-mm ID cuffed tube

550. What is the recommended pediatric dose of epinephrine?
  A. 0.1 mL/kg of 1 : 10,000
  B. 0.5 mL/kg of 1 : 1,000
  C. 0.1 mL/kg of 1 : 10,000
  D. 0.5 mL/kg of 1 : 1,000
  E. 1.0 mL/kg of 1 : 10,000

551. Which routes of administration may be used to give epinephrine to a pediatric patient?
  1. Intraosseous
  2. Intravenous
  3. Endotracheal tube
  4. Intracardiac
     A. 2, 3, and 4
     B. 1 and 2
     C. 1, 2, and 4
     D. 2 only
     E. All of the above

552. What is the recommended pediatric dose of lidocaine that can be given intravenously?
     A. 0.5 mg/kg
     B. 1 mg/kg
     C. 2 mg/kg
     D. 25 mg
     E. 50 mg

553. To deliver a dopamine infusion of 10 mg/kg min to a 20 kg infant, how much dopamine would be added to 100 mL of fluid and how fast should the IV be run?
     A. 30 mg, 10 cc/min
     B. 60 mg, 10 cc/h
     C. 90 mg, 10 cc/min
     D. 120 mg, 10 cc/h
     E. 240 mg, 10 cc/h

554. The recommended dose of sodium bicarbonate for a child is
     A. 0.5 mEq/kg
     B. 1.0 mEq/kg
     C. 2.0 mEq/kg
     D. 2.5 mEq/kg
     E. 5.0 mEq/kg

555. The narrowest point of a child's airway is the
   A. carina
   B. cricoid cartilage
   C. epiglottis
   D. vocal cords
   E. Arytenoid cartilage

556. A serious threat to the patient with acute epiglottitis would be
   A. humidified oxygen, high percentage
   B. steam from a shower or bath
   C. an oxygen mask at 8 L/min
   D. examination of the oropharynx with a tongue depressor
   E. auscultation of the chest with a cold stethoscope

557. You answer a call concerning a child in respiratory distress. On examination, you find a febrile, 22-month-old boy with stridor. He is sitting upright with head forward and drooling. The respiratory rate is 46 with nasal flaring and suprasternal retractions. His mother tells you that he has been sick like this for about 2 hours, and that he has a fever of 103.4°F. He is sitting forward and drooling slightly. From these observations you suspect that the child is experiencing
   A. epiglottitis
   B. croup
   C. foreign body aspiration
   D. bronchiolitis
   E. pneumonia

558. You respond to a call about an 8-month-old child in respiratory distress. The child has intercostal retractions and nasal flaring with a respiratory rate of 50. The child has a temperature of 100.9°F rectally. On auscultation you hear expiratory wheezes in all lung fields. Which is most likely?
   A. Asthma
   B. Foreign body aspiration
   C. Bronchiolitis
   D. Croup
   E. Pneumonia

559. For young children, the most dependable early sign of hypovolemia is
A. a marked decrease in activity
B. tachycardia
C. change in color
D. decrease in BP
E. bradycardia

560. In what age range would you place a baby who does not object to having clothes removed, is easily distracted by a rattle, and fusses when the mother tries to move away?
A. Newborn
B. 1–6 months
C. 6–12 months
D. 18–36 months
E. 3–5 years

561. In what age range would you place a baby who clings to his mother, fusses when you approach to listen to his chest, and is frightened by direct eye contact with you?
A. Newborn
B. 1–6 months
C. 6–12 months
D. 18–36 months
E. 4–5 years

562. What is the normal respiratory rate for a 3-month-old?
A. 8–12 breaths per minute
B. 15–20 breaths per minute
C. 20–25 breaths per minute
D. 20–40 breaths per minute
E. 30–50 breaths per minute

563. What is the normal resting pulse for a 4-month-old?
A. 60 beats per minute
B. 80 beats per minute
C. 90 beats per minute
D. 100 beats per minute
E. 120 beats per minute

564. You respond to a call concerning a child who has had a sudden onset of difficulty in breathing. Your assessment reveals a 24-month-old child in no distress. The mother tells you that her child had suddenly turned blue and started to gasp and that this was followed by a bit of coughing. Afterward the child improved. You should
   A. reassure the mother
   B. transport the child to the hospital immediately
   C. advise the mother to take the child to her family doctor in the morning
   D. advise the mother to take the child to a free-standing clinic today
   E. advise the mother to take the child to her pediatrician's office this afternoon

365. A healthy 1-year-old breathes about
   A. 10–20 times per minute
   B. 20–30 times per minute
   C. 30–40 times per minute
   D. 40–50 times per minute
   E. 50–60 times per minute

566. What is the normal blood pressure of a 1-year-old child?
   A. 60/30
   B. 75/50
   C. 95/65
   D. 120/80
   E. 140/80

567. In infants, you should use a bag–valve–mask ventilating device with a volume of
   A. 1,000–1,500 mL
   B. 750–1,000 mL
   C. 250–500 mL
   D. 100–200 mL
   E. 75–100 mL

568. What is true about sudden infant death syndrome (SIDS)?
 A. SIDS can now be accurately predicted or prevented by careful monitoring of the child.
 B. Usually, no attempt should be made to resuscitate the obviously dead child.
 C. There is often substantial signs of parental neglect, and the parents should be confronted with this possibility.
 D. The cause of SIDS is not yet known.
 E. SIDS often occurs during the early afternoon.

569. Which of the following is NOT part of routine care for a newborn child?
 A. Monitor respirations
 B. Prevention of hypothermia
 C. Determine APGAR score
 D. Monitor the ECG
 E. Clear the airway

570. Which of the following is NOT part of Apgar scoring?
 A. Appearance
 B. Pulse
 C. Grip strength
 D. Activity
 E. Respiratory effort

571. Which of the following statements is NOT true about child abuse?
 A. The child may have injuries about the mouth.
 B. The child may not cry, despite being injured.
 C. The parents may give conflicting stories about the injury.
 D. The child is being cuddled protectively by mother.
 E. There are both old and new abrasions and contusions.

572. In an infant under the age of 1 year, all of the following are
signs of dehydration EXCEPT
A. decreased skin turgor
B. depressed fontanelles
C. oliguria
D. decreased blood pressure
E. apathy and listlessness

573. Children are more vulnerable than adults to
A. pulmonary contusion
B. pericardial tamponade
C. liver injuries
D. spleen injuries
E. all of the above

574. Which size of larygoscope blade is appropriate for a 3- to
9-year-old child?
A. 0 Wis – Hipple
B. 1 Miller
C. 1.5 Macintosh
D. 2 Miller
E. 3 Macintosh

Explanatory Answers

539. D. Unfortunately, in our country, accidents are the main cause of death for children 1 to 14. Infections claim the most children under 1 year old. (Ref. Caroline, p. 518)

540. E. In a child, any IV line that is readily available is preferred! (Ref. ACLS, p. 263)

541. D. Defibrillation requires much lower energy in the child than in the adult. (Ref. ACLS, p. 267)

542. A. A child should not be separated from his or her parents if at all possible. It is cruel and unusual punishment to separate a child from his or her most significant source of comfort and reassurance when he or she is ill or injured. Provision should be made for a mother or father to ride with the child in the ambulance, particularly for a critically ill child. (Remember that you are a threat to the child). (Ref. Caroline, p. 505)

543. E. A silent chest means that there is poor air exchange and is an ominous finding. This finding is most often seen in severe asthma but may also be found in foreign-body airway obstruction, croup, and epiglottitis. These children will have the other signs of severe respiratory distress, such as intercostal and neck retractions and abdominal breathing. A silent chest connotates *severe respiratory distress.* (Ref. Caroline, p. 511)

544. D. Croup only infrequently requires hospitalization, much less tracheostomy or intubation. Field therapy of croup is aimed at airway maintainance and oxygenation. Physicians may prescribe steroids or racemic epinephrine for treatment of severe croup. (Ref. Caroline, p. 513)

545. A. The pediatric patient more often suffers a respiratory arrest, so the bradycardia and block characteristic of hypoxia will more frequently be found. (Ref. ACLS, p. 268)

546. B. In general, bronchiolitis does not respond well to epinephrine, in contrast to asthma's good response. Inhaled bronchodilators such as Ventolin are more effective in treatment of bron-cholitis. Asthma is almost never seen in children under 1 year of age, while bronchiolitis (or bronchospastic airway disorder) is often seen. (Ref. Caroline, p. 512)

547. A. It is often difficult, even for an experienced physician, to clinically differentiate croup from epiglottitis. Many of the signs and symptoms of early epiglottitis are similar to those of croup. Pain on swallowing, however, is not usually found in croup, but is common in epiglottitis. *Note*: This is not an iron-clad rule. Until the X-rays are available, both should be considered in any child who presents with an acute onset of respiratory distress. (Ref. Caroline, p. 514)

548. D. The maximum dose of atropine for a child should be 1.0 mg. The appropriate dose for a child should be about 0.01 mg/kg. (Ref. ACLS, p. 265)

549. D. For a 2- to 3-year-old child, an endotracheal tube about 4.5–5.0 internal diameter (ID) is appropriate. A rough rule of thumb to approximate the tube size in infants and small children is to use a tube about the size of the child's little finger for the first attempt. Another rough rule of thumb is to choose a tube with ID = (16 + age)/4 (18/4 = 4.5). *Never* use a cuffed tube on chil-dren younger than 8 years old. (Ref. ACLS, p. 262; Caroline, p. 531)

550. A. The appropriate dose of epinephrine for a child is 0.1 cc/kg of a 1:10,000 solution. (Ref. ACLS, p. 265)

551. C. Intracardiac injections are hazardous and should be avoided if at all possible. (Ref. ACLS, p. 265)

552. B. As in adults, lidocaine should be given in 1 mg/kg doses. (Ref. ACLS, p. 268)

553. B. 120 mg in 100 cc is equal to 12 mg/cc. At 60 drops/cc, each drop contains 0.2 mg or 200 μg. A starting dose of 10 μg/kg would therefore be about 1 drop/min or 10 cc/h. (Ref. ACLS, p. 266)

554. B. A child's dose of bicarbonate, like that for an adult, should be 1.0 mEq/kg. The child's dose should be diluted to half the adult strength, to prevent possible osmotic overload. (Ref. ACLS, p. 265)

555. B. The narrowest part of a child's airway is the cricoid cartilage. This is why we can use an uncuffed tube in children, while we need a cuffed tube in adults. (Ref. ACLS, p. 262)

556. D. Never, never attempt to examine the throat or oropharynx of a child with epiglottitis until the preparations are complete for both intubation and a surgical airway. In short, don't do it in the field, ever. (Ref. Caroline, p. 514)

557. A. This is the typical presentation of the patient with acute epiglottitis. The illness is acute and the child often appears toxic. The child frequently sits bolt upright, drools, and is anxious. (Ref. Caroline, p. 415)

558. C. Bronchiolitis produces essentially the same clinical picture as asthma but occurs in children under the age of 2. Bronchiolitis is often caused by a viral infection and usually is has associated with a low-grade temperature. (Ref. Caroline, p. 513)

559. B. A child will maintain the blood pressure until nearly 30% of the total blood volume is lost. The most frequent sign associated with shock in children is a tachycardia. Unfortunately, many paramedics do not know how the pulse rates change with age and do not readily recognize shock in children. (Ref. Caroline, pp. 518–519)

560. C. The 6- to 12-month-old child fusses when the most significant person, usually the mother, moves away. These children are otherwise usually easy to manage and easily allow you to distract them and then remove their clothes. (Ref. Caroline, p. 504)

561. D. The 18- to 36-month-old is in "the terrible twos". They fuss with most examiners and can be quite difficult. (Ref. Caroline, pp. 504–505)

562. D. The normal respiratory rate for the young child who is from 1 month to 1 year old is about 20 to 40 respirations per minute. Needless to say, the rate is higher for those who are younger and lower for the 1-year-olds. (Ref. Caroline, p. 519)

563. E. Vital signs in children are actually quite important and usually ignored for a variety of reasons. The wise paramedic knows the normal pulse at all ages. (Ref. Caroline, p. 519)

564. B. This is a typical picture of a patient with an acutely aspirated foreign body. Health providers and parents can be lulled into a false sense of security by the latent period between aspiration and the results of the lung obstruction. This patient needs to go to a full-service emergency department. (Ref. Caroline, p. 507)

565. B. This is an often-missed and important piece of data. It is included so that you do not forget that the respiratory rate of a child should be measured, if at all possible. Crying is not an excuse for ignoring the respiratory note. (Ref. Nelson, p. 32)

566. C. Like the respiratory rate, the normal blood pressure is often not obtained by our colleagues. (You, of course, get a BP on EVERY child, right.) (Ref. Nelson, p. 1354)

567. C. In infants, a bag volume of about 250–500 cc is ideal. Larger bags make it difficult to regulate the smaller tidal volumes, while smaller bags simply do not deliver enough. (Ref. ACLS, p. 262)

568. D. The cause of SIDS is not yet known. We do know that there is usually no sign of parental neglect and that the child dies during sleep. An attempt should be made to resuscitate the child. It is important that the family feel that everything possible has been done to save the child. (Ref. Caroline, p. 515)

569. D. Normally, the child will not need ECG monitoring. Monitoring respirations is appropriate and can be done during determination of the Apgar score. Needless to say, airway maintenance is always important. All newborns are susceptible to hypothermia and should be covered. (Ref. Caroline, pp. 590–596)

570. C. Apgar scoring is a score of appearance, pulse, grimace, activity, and respiratory effort. It is usually done at 1 and 5 minutes after birth. Each sign is given a score of 0, 1, or 2. A total score of 9 or 10 is excellent, while 4 to 6 means that the child is in need of resuscitation. (Ref. Caroline, p. 496)

571. D. Children who have been abused are often carried like a loaf of bread, rather than being cuddled. A child that snuggles to a parent is not likely to have been abused consistently by that parent. (Needless to say, the baby-sitter, elder siblings, other parent, "friends of the family," etc., are not above suspicion.) (Ref. Caroline, p. 516)

572. D. Dehydrated sick children are different. They look listless, have decreased skin turgor, and the fontanelles are depressed if they are still open. The child frequently has scanty urine output and does not tear with crying. They don't drop their blood pressure until the bitter end. (Ref. Caroline, p. 518)

573. E. Since children have less padding and lower diaphragms, the abdominal contents are more vulnerable to trauma, including the liver and spleen. Likewise, the thorax is more pliable in the child, and pulmonary and cardiac injuries are correspondingly more severe. (Ref. Caroline, pp. 518–519)

574. D. Generally, a straight blade is more effective in children. The size of the blade can be roughly approximated by

Age	Blade size
"Premie"	0
Newborn–1 year	1
1–3 years	1.5
3–9 Years	2
Over 9 Years	3 (or 4)

(Ref. Caroline, p. 531)

15 Environmental Injuries

575. How does the skin regulate body temperature?
    1. The dermis expands and contracts.
    2. Perspiration evaporates.
    3. Heat from the liver, heart, and brain is transferred to the skin's surface.
    4. Heat from the blood vessels under the skin is radiated to the surface.
       A. All of the above
       B. 2, 3, and 4
       C. 1, 2, and 4
       E. 2 and 4

576. Which statements are true of electrical burns?
    1. The power company should be called immediately if there are fallen wires or other electrical hazards.
    2. Respiratory and cardiac arrest are the major problems of victims with electrical burns.
    3. Electrical burns can be more serious than they appear.
    4. Often there are entry and exit burns from where the electricity enters and exits the body.
       A. 1, 2, and 3
       B. 1 and 4
       C. 1, 2, and 4
       D. All of the above
       E. None of the above

231

577. You are caring for a firefighter who has just been trapped by falling debris in a house fire. He was promptly rescued and appears to have no significant external injuries. He did lose his protective mask, however. What is the MOST IMPORTANT delayed complication this firefighter may experience?
    A. Second-degree burns of the face
    B. Congestive heart failure
    C. Injury to the lungs as a result of pulmonary edema
    D. Hypoxic injury to the brain or heart
    E. Gastrointestinal bleeding

578. Which factor does not affect the outcome in near drowning?
    A. Age of the patient
    B. Depth of the water
    C. Amount of fluid aspirated
    D. Underlying heart and lung disease
    E. Temperature of the water

579. The red blood cells take up carbon monoxide approximately
    A. 500 times more readily than oxygen
    B. 200 times more readily than oxygen
    C. 50 times more readily than oxygen
    D. at the same rate as oxygen
    E. twice as fast as oxygen

580. Which is the most serious heat-related emergency?
    A. Heat cramps
    B. Heat exhaustion
    C. Heat stroke
    D. Miliaria
    E. All of the above are equally serious

581. An EMT–paramedic responds to a call to find a construction worker who has collapsed. The temperature outside is 96°F with a humidity of 92%. The victim's respirations are rapid and shallow; his skin is pale and clammy. This profusely perspiring individual appears weak and dizzy. You suspect
   A. heat exhaustion
   B. heat syncope
   C. heat stroke
   D. heat cramps
   E. miliaria

582. In the situation described in the preceding question, what action should be undertaken?
   1. Remove as much clothing as possible.
   2. Wet the patient down with cold water.
   3. Administer aspirin.
   4. Transport the victim to a hospital as soon as possible.
   A. 1, 2, and 3
   B. 1 and 2 only
   C. 1, 2, and 4
   D. 4 only
   E. All of the above

583. In the patient with severe hypothermia, motion, CPR, jostling, or central line placement may trigger what dysrhythmia?
   A. Paroxysmal atrial tachycardia
   B. Ventricular fibrillation
   C. Ventricular tachycardia
   D. Asystole
   E. Atrial fibrillation

584. What weather conditions are most likely to lead to heat exhaustion?
   A. High temperature, low humidity, and a stiff breeze
   B. High temperature and humidity with little or no breeze
   C. High temperature, low humidity, and no breeze
   D. High temperature and humidity with a stiff breeze

585. How would you treat a patient with frostbite who is several hours from a hospital?

1. Transport the victim to a hospital as soon as possible.
2. Start rewarming by immersing the affected part in warm (104°F) water.
3. Cover the injured area with dry, sterile dressings.
4. Remove all wet clothing.
   - **A.** 1 and 3
   - **B.** 1, 3, and 4
   - **C.** 2 and 4
   - **D.** 4 only
   - **E.** All of the above

586. The first sign of frostbite is
   - **A.** numbing and reddening of exposed skin surfaces
   - **B.** dead white skin
   - **C.** skin that appears blue
   - **D.** skin that appears blotchy white or gray and is edematous
   - **E.** blister formation

587. You are called to a fruit farm about 12 miles from your station. The farm manager takes you to see one of the temporary workers who is not feeling well. On examination you find a man who is pale, profusely sweating, and coughing up watery sputum. The vital signs are BP 152/90, pulse 52 and slightly irregular, and respirations 30 and shallow. His pupils are constricted and there is no JVD. When listening to the chest you hear scattered wheezes throughout. On observation, you notice that the muscles of the extremities are finely twitching. The victim appears to be in distress and has soiled his pants. While talking with the farm manager, you are told that the patient has been spraying insecticides over the last few days. Your treatment should include all but
   - **A.** administration of morphine 5–10 mg in a slow IV
   - **B.** starting an IV with D_5W
   - **C.** administration of atropine 2 mg IM
   - **D.** removal of the patient's clothes
   - **E.** administration of oxygen at a high concentration

588. Fifteen minutes before you arrived, a 22-year-old woman swallowed 50 over-the-counter sleeping pills. She is alert but weeping. Her vital signs are BP 120/80, pulse 95, and respirations 16. Though slightly dilated, her pupils are reactive. The rest of the physical examination is normal. Which statement is true of this case?

    A. Induction of vomiting is more effective than gastric lavage in emptying this patient's stomach.

    B. Gastric lavage through a nasogastric tube is the preferred method of emptying this patient's stomach.

    C. An antidote needs to be given before any other treatment is undertaken.

    D. So it has time to work, activated charcoal should be given first if syrup of ipecac is used.

    E. A nasogastric tube should NEVER be passed when the patient is intubated, because of the pressure on the esophagus.

589. A patient received second-degree burns on his chest and on the extensor and flexor surfaces of his forearms while trying to start a barbeque grill with gasoline. What percentage of his body has been burned?

    A. 36

    B. 33

    C. 27

    D. 22

    E. 18

590. When treating a patient who has suffered second-degree burns over 10% of her body (no respiratory involvement), you may do which of the following?

    1. Allow the patient to have something to drink.

    2. Apply oil-based ointments.

    3. Apply moist, sterile dressings.

    4. Apply dry, sterile dressings.

        A. All of the above

        B. 1, 3, and 4

        C. 1 and 4

        D. 2, 3, and 4

        E. None of the above

591. To remove dry chemicals that can cause chemical burns, you should
   A. brush the chemical off, and then cover the area with a sterile dressing
   B. brush the chemical off, and then flush the area with copious amounts of water
   C. clean the area with vinegar followed by a water rinse
   D. apply an oil-based baking soda solution, then cover with a sterile dressing
   E. use alcohol to remove the chemical without water

592. Your patient appears to have bright cherry red lips after being moved from a closed garage where he was working on his car. What is the most likely cause of this bright coloring?
   A. Hypoxia
   B. Overoxygenation
   C. Inhalation of carbon dioxide
   D. Displacement of the oxygen in the hemoglobin by carbon monoxide
   E. Vasodilation caused by freon fumes from the air-conditioning

593. When treating a victim from a gas refinery explosion, first priority should be given to
   A. airway management
   B. soft tissue injuries
   C. possible fractures
   D. burn treatment
   E. cervical spine injuries

594. Hot, dry skin can be an indication of
   A. loss of body hair
   B. heat stroke
   C. heat anaphylaxis
   D. shock
   E. organophosphate poisoning

Explanatory Answers

575. B. The body will maintain the normal temperature against heat stress until all reserves are exhausted. These defenses include perspiration, transfer of heat from core organs to the skin, and vasodilation of skin surface vessels to facilitate radiation of heat. If the body becomes dehydrated, other reflexes will attempt to preserve the blood pressure at the expense of heat regulation. At this point, heat illness can result. If the body's defenses are rapidly overwhelmed, heat illness can result without the dehydration. (Ref. Caroline, pp. 425, 426, 429)

576. D. Electrical burns frequently (but not always) have both an exit and an entrance wound. Major injuries often do not occur at the entrance point, but rather as the electrical current traverses muscles, bone, blood vessels, and nerves from the entrance to the exit point. If the path includes the heart or central nervous system (a common occurrence when the patient grasps a "hot" wire) a respiratory or cardiac arrest may occur. High-tension lines should be handled ONLY with currently certified equipment and proper training. As most EMTs and paramedics do not have the specialized equipment or training to manage high-tension electrical lines, they should have the power company respond to the accident to manage these lines. (Ref. Caroline, pp. 386–387)

577. D. With CO poisoning, hypoxia occurs as a result of displacement of oxygen from hemoglobin by the carbon monoxide. This hypoxia can cause myocardial infarction or severe neurologic damage. Not listed but equally important is upper airway edema, which can develop rapidly in the patient with a toxic inhalation. These patients require exceptionally careful monitoring. (Ref. Caroline, pp. 211, 449–450)

578. B. This is an easy one. You drown just as dead in an inch of water as in an ocean. (Ref. Caroline, p. 209–211)

579. B. Because it has 200 times more affinity for hemoglobin than oxygen, anything that increases oxygen consumption increases the rapidity of action of CO. (Ref. Caroline, p. 449–450)

580. C. Heat stroke occurs when the body's defenses against heat stress have been completely overwhelmed. Without proper care, the patient will die shortly. It is the most important emergency listed. (Ref. Caroline, p. 428)

581. C. Decreased level of consciousness and exposure to heat stress equal heat stroke until proven otherwise. Remember that not *all* heat stroke is hot and dry. Exertional heat stroke victims are sweating profusely 30–50% of the time. (Ref. Caroline, p. 428)

582. C. Aspirin does not help the patient with heat stroke. External cooling is needed when the internal systems have been overwhelmed with heat stress. (Ref. Caroline, p. 428)

583. B. People who are severely hypothermic who are resuscitated often have ventricular fibrillation as the terminal event. Without resuscitation, the same patient will often die in asystole as the core temperature falls. Movement or jostling will often trigger ventricular fibrillation in the very vulnerable cold myocardium. (Ref. Caroline, p. 430)

584. B. Obviously if the wind is not blowing, and the humidity is high, the cooling effect of evaporation is nullified. (Ref. Caroline, pp. 425–428)

585. E. Treatment of frostbite depends, to some extent, on how far you have to go before the patient has definitive medical care. If the patient is several hours from a medical facility, field rewarming is appropriate. Ensure that there is no possibility of refreezing. (Ref. Caroline, p. 432)

586. A. As the skin surface becomes cold, it is anesthetized and becomes somewhat reddened. As the frostbite progresses, the color changes to white. Blister formation occurs 1 to 3 days after the injury. (Ref. Caroline, p. 432)

587. A. This scenario represents the "SLUD" toxidrome — salivation, lacrimation, urination, and defecation — and is associated with cholinesterase inhibitor–type insecticides. Although rales are present, and may be indicative of pulmonary edema, the use of morphine in this patient is not indicated. All of the other answers are appropriate treatments. (Ref. Caroline, p. 451)

588. A. Ipecac-induced vomiting generally rids the stomach of more pills and pill fragments than gastric lavage. The latter may enhance absorption by flushing fragments into the small intestine. (Ref. Caroline, p. 447)

589. C. Rule of 9's: 18% for the front of the chest and one half of 9% for each forearm—4.5% for right arm and 4.5% for left arm. Total = 27%. (Ref. Caroline, p. 383)

590. B. The only contraindication for burn dressings is "goo." Do not use oil, butter, creams, or spray. Note that many authorities do not want to have the patient in wet dressings. This is particularly true for those who handle pediatric patients or use air ambulances extensively. The wet dressings may evaporate and cause severe hypothermia. (Ref. Caroline, p. 383)

591. B. This is a bit tricky, even in real life. Any chemical that causes burns should be removed immediately. The most logical way to proceed with a dry chemical is to brush as much of the chemical off as possible, then irrigate the area with copious amounts of water. The "problem" that most EMS authorities worry about is activation of the chemical by water. It is not logical to neglect the normal sweating of the body and the subsequent activation of lime by this mechanism. (It is obvious to me that the author that advocates only brushing has never worked with lime or cement in a hot and humid climate.) Indeed, it is illogical NOT to irrigate the area and reduce the concentration of the chemical at the site of this sweating. As in ALL chemical injuries with water-soluble chemicals, COPIOUS irrigation is indicated. (Ref. Caroline, p. 386)

592. D. The classic bright red coloring is most often seen as a postmortem finding. It is rather rare in survivors. Indeed, the most common findings in carbon monoxide poisoning are headache and nausea. (Ref. Caroline, p. 450)

593. A. Always airway first. If he does not breathe, you do not have a patient (for long). (Ref. Caroline, p. 43)

594. B. Hot dry skin is indicative of classic (but not exertional) heat stroke. It is not seen with shock, organophospate poisoning, or loss of body hair. To the best of my knowledge, there is no such thing as heat anaphylaxia. (Ref. Caroline, p. 428)

16 Psychological Problems and Special Patients

QUESTIONS 595–600: Select the ONE most appropriate answer.

595. One of the most common errors made by new paramedics is
    A. inappropriate calmness
    B. failure to focus on individual injuries
    C. rendering care above their level of competence
    D. lack of concern for patients
    E. "freezing"

596. Informed consent implies that the patient knows who you are, your level of training or credentials, and what you plan to do. It is best obtained
    A. by court order
    B. by police order
    C. by verbal consent
    D. by a signed consent form
    E. by the patient's nearest living relative in all cases

597. The parents of a seriously injured child are not available and cannot be reached. You may assume that
  A. inferred consent is granted
  B. informed consent is granted
  C. inherent consent is granted
  D. implied consent is granted
  E. implied consent will be denied unless you reach the patient's guardians; you must obtain a court order when you are unable to reach the parents

598. Mentally retarded, insane, or incompetent patients may be treated without consent under the principle of
  A. implied consent
  B. informed consent
  C. the Good Samaritan Law
  D. the mental health statute of 1904
  E. the principle of abandonment

599. When you are to transport an emotionally disturbed patient, you should
  A. use physical restraints if indicated by your judgment
  B. use physical restraints if requested by the family
  C. always restrain the patient for everybody's safety
  D. wait for police assistance
  E. assume that chemical restraints will be needed

600. A patient has been bitten by a stray dog. Your most important action is to
  A. find the owner of the dog
  B. prevent the animal from biting others
  C. kill the animal and preserve the head
  D. determine if the dog is rabid
  E. call the police

Explanatory Answers

595. C. Indeed, the most common error made by new practitioners at all levels from EMT to physician is to attempt to do more than they are qualified or trained to do. Peter Rosen describes it as a "technical imperative." He notes that if new practitioners are trained to do something, and allowed to do it freely, you will find that they find more frequent indications to do it than expected. (Ref. Brady, p. 13; AAOS, p. 7)

596. D. Informed consent must be obtained from the patient who is over the age of 18, and from the parents in certain cases of patients under the age of 18. For certain diseases and emergencies, some states allow "emancipated minors" to give their own consent. In all cases where informed consent is obtained, it is best done in writing, when possible. (Ref. Brady, pp. 2, 15; AAOS, p. 16)

597. D. Implied consent may be interpreted to mean that the paramedic can assume that in a similar situation, if the parents were available, they would act to preserve the life of their child. It is used only for life- or limb-threatening emergencies, as not all parents can be assumed to want their child treated in minor cases. (Ref. Brady, p. 16; AAOS, p. 17)

598. A. The principle of implied consent covers not only minors, but also anyone else who is unable to actively give consent. (Ref. Brady, p. 17; AAOS, p. 17)

599. D. By and large, when the patient needs to be restrained, you need help. The closest and often most experienced help is your police force. Do not hesitate to use them. (Ref. Brady, p. 17; AAOS, p. 451)

600. B. The most important thing you can do at this point is to ensure that you do not collect any more casualties. Protect your patients and yourself. (Ref. Brady, p. 17; AAOS, p. 305)

References

AAOS: American Academy of Orthopedic Surgeons: *Emergency Care and Transportation of the Sick and Injured,* ed. 4. Park Ridge, IL, ORCO, 1987.

Abbott: Abbott J, Gifford M, Rosen P: *Protocols for Prehospital Emergency Medical Care,* ed 2. Baltimore, Williams and Wilkins, 1984.

ACLS: American Heart Association: *Textbook of Advanced Cardiac Life Support,* Dallas, 1987.

BTLS: Campbell JE: *Basic Trauma Life Support — Advanced Prehospital Care.* Englewood Cliffs, NJ, Brady, 1985.

Caroline: Caroline NL: *Emergency Care in the Streets,* ed 3. Boston, Little, Brown, 1987.

Grant: Grant HD, Murray RH, Bergeron JD: *Emergency Care,* ed 4. Englewood Cliffs, NJ, Brady, 1986.

Nelson: Nelson. *Textbook of Pediatrics,* ed 11. Philadelphia, WB Saunders, 1979.